ARRL's

VoIP: Internet Linking for Radio Amateurs

Jonathan Taylor, K1RFD

D1315107

Published by
ARRL—the national association for Amateur Radio
Newington, CT 06111 USA

CONTENTS

FOREWORD

When the Internet burst onto the public stage in the early 1990s, some amateurs were fearful. They worried that the Internet would somehow replace the avocation that they had grown to love.

In the years that followed, however, it quickly became clear that the Internet was *complementing* Amateur Radio, not replacing it. Hams put the Internet to work as a medium for rapid exchange of information and ideas. Advances in digital amateur communication and software-defined radio had their genesis in exchanges that took place on the Internet.

Amateurs also realized that the Internet could serve as a communications "pipeline" to link distant locations in a reliable manner that isn't always possible with satellites or HF communication. Thanks to amateur ingenuity, we now have new communication systems that unite radio with the Internet in ways never imagined just a few years ago.

One system uses Voice Over Internet Protocol, or *VoIP*, to exchange voice communication using the Internet to bridge individual radio stations. By using VoIP networks, hams who were once limited to local communication because of antenna restrictions and other issues can now talk to the world.

VoIP: Internet Linking for Radio Amateurs is your guide to VoIP. The author is Jonathan Taylor, K1RFD, the creator of *EchoLink*, one of the most popular amateur VoIP networks. But Jonathan doesn't confine this book to a discussion of *EchoLink*. On the contrary, *VoIP: Internet Linking for Radio Amateurs* explores other systems in detail, including the Internet Radio Linking Project, (*IRLP*), *eQSO* and *WIRES*.

VoIP: Internet Linking for Radio Amateurs is written in way that any amateur can understand, regardless of technical ability. In this book, you find a wealth of helpful information to make your VoIP experience as enjoyable as possible.

Please take a few minutes to give us your comments and suggestions on this book. There's a handy Feedback Form for this purpose at the back, or you can send e-mail to: **pubsfdbk@arrl.org**.

David Sumner, K1ZZ
Executive Vice President
Newington, Connecticut
March 2004

Chapter 1

Connecting the World

Hurricane Isabel slams into the coast of North Carolina, unleashing 95-knot winds and a six-foot storm surge, knocking out electric power and local telephone communications. Despite unfavorable HF propagation, local weather reports are relayed by Amateur Radio operators, using hand-held radios, directly to the National Hurricane Center in Florida. Damage reports and health-and-welfare information is routed directly to emergency operations centers and Red Cross centers hundreds of miles away. Amateur Radio steps in when many other communications systems fail.

The space shuttle *Columbia* disintegrates over eastern Texas, scattering debris over a broad swath. Radio amateurs spring into action, locating debris and exchanging precise location reports with hams in nearby counties, who are assisting local law enforcement and NASA. Questions about *Columbia's* demise are quickly getting answers.

A retired electrical engineer who had been an active member of his local radio club in the Northeast begins a new life in Florida, and faces the prospect of remaining out of touch with old friends because of strict outdoor antenna restrictions. But he still manages to check into his club's daily 2-meter net back home, just as if he'd never left. Friendships strengthened by Amateur Radio remain strong as ever.

All of this is made possible by an intriguing marriage of perhaps the two greatest communications inventions of the twentieth century: Radio and the Internet. Hams in the twenty-first century now find themselves in the perfect position to join these two technologies together. Through a technique called *Internet linking*, they are harnessing the immediacy and portability of radio communication to the global reach of the Internet, and all sorts of new possibilities are emerging.

STRANGE BEDFELLOWS?

Amateur Radio has more in common with the Internet than you might realize. Today's Internet began as the vision of DARPA, the US Government's Defense Advanced Research Projects Agency. The idea was to create a coast-to-coast digital network which could route messages from anywhere to anywhere, with plenty of extra paths in place so that the whole thing would hold together even after a nuclear weapons strike, or a devastating natural disaster. Even back in the 1970s, the system worked well. Colleges and universities began hooking up their computers to ARPANET, finding it a cost-effective way to exchange research information. Large corporations began using the network—which now spanned the globe, and had become known as the Internet—to exchange e-mail. Then, in the early 1990s, the invention of the graphical Web browser ignited an explosion of Internet usage. Millions and millions of computers are now interconnected, many of which are PCs in homes.

Amateur Radio, although it hasn't seen the same growth spurt (imagine the interference!), is also global, immediate, and fault-tolerant. We already know that hams are sometimes the only link to the outside world from the site of a disaster, with mobile and portable stations often proving most valuable to relay traffic directly from the scene.

So why not experiment with connecting the two together?

Some enterprising hams had exactly this thought in the mid-1990s, when the Internet began coming into homes in earnest, and thus also into ham shacks. The idea was this: Using personal computers equipped with sound cards, connect the audio signals of two FM rigs to each other over the Internet. This allows mobile and portable stations in the coverage area of one station to establish voice communication with stations in the coverage area of the other, without limitations imposed by distance, terrain, or HF propagation (**Figure 1.1**).

Sending data (including voice signals) over the Internet is certainly nothing new. What makes this idea interesting is that Amateur Radio stations can harness this technology to produce a hybrid system that is part RF and part Internet, taking advantage of the inherent strengths of both techniques.

EARLY EXPERIMENTS

In the mid 1990s, a program called *Internet Phone* began to make the rounds. It was one of the first voice-over-IP (VoIP) programs widely available to the public. The idea was that you could use the microphone and speaker connected to your Internet-attached PC to make telephone calls to any similarly equipped computer anywhere in the world, free! As long as you knew the Internet address of the computer you wanted to hook up with, you could simply type it in, establish a connection and start talking. Sure,

Figure 1.1—By interconnecting two FM simplex stations over the Internet, the coverage areas of the two stations are effectively combined.

there were occasional "drop outs" (gaps in the audio) due to the slow modems at each end, but the experience of hearing someone else's voice coming from the computer speakers was stunning.

Naturally, once a few enterprising hams began experimenting with *Internet Phone*, they got the idea that it could easily be adapted to join VHF-FM stations together. Rather than connecting a microphone and speakers to the computer's sound card, why not connect the sound card to the microphone and speaker jacks of an FM transceiver? This would allow anyone within range of the transceiver connected to Computer A to communicate with anyone within range of the rig connected to Computer B. Sure enough, it worked (sort of), and one of the first Internet voice links between two amateur stations was established.

The next logical step was to tune the "linked" transceiver to the frequency pair of a local repeater, rather than a simplex frequency. This opened up even more possibilities, since now any station in range of the repeater at either end could be part of the long-distance QSO. Things were starting to get interesting!

In 1996, Mark Brown, N9YNQ, developed a *Windows* program called *Repeater Link*. *Repeater Link* formed a software bridge between *Internet Phone* and an FM rig connected to the PC through a special hardware interface concocted by Jack Leverich, KC9KY. The *Repeater Link* system may have been the first PC-based Amateur Radio VoIP linking system. (Perhaps Mark and Jack can lay claim to being the Alexander Graham Bell and Thomas Watson of Internet linking.)

Unfortunately, like many early Internet experiments, technology took a while to catch up. There was plenty of talk about broadband Internet access in the mid-90s, and not very much action. (Remember ISDN service from the telephone company? The running joke was that ISDN actually stood for "It Still Does Nothing"). Without reliable, dedicated Internet access coming into the ham shack or the repeater site, widespread Internet linking would have to wait.

Fortunately, broadband did finally arrive, and so did fast, cheap personal computers. Today, millions of Americans have Internet access in their homes delivered by TV cable, digital subscriber line (DSL) or satellite. Dial-up modems have improved, too, as have the quality of (some) phone lines. Coming from the opposite direction, audio and video compression technologies have improved, and personal computers are more efficient than ever before at processing this information, and quite a bit cheaper, cycle for cycle.

LET THE LINKING BEGIN!

Fueled partly by the improvements in Internet bandwidth, more voice-over-IP Internet linking systems began to spring up. One of the most successful was (and still is) the Internet Radio Linking Project, or *IRLP*. *IRLP* begin experimenting in the fall of 1997 with using the Internet to link several amateur systems in Canada, with the first full-time hookup running coast-to-coast between Vancouver and Saint John, New Brunswick. After a few false starts, Dave Cameron, VE7LTD, settled on the open-source operating system called *Linux* as the platform for the next generation of *IRLP*. Since then, *IRLP* has flourished into a reliable, worldwide network, with more than 1200 repeaters and simplex stations in early 2004.

A few other enterprising hams continued experimenting with *Windows*-based systems, on which the original *Internet Phone* experiments had been conducted. In 2001, Graeme Barnes, MØCSH, developed a program called *iLINK,* which had two compelling features: It allowed access directly from a desktop computer, and it worked remarkably well over conventional dial-up Internet connections. This helped put Internet linking in the hands of thousands of hams who already had *Windows*-based computers and dial-up Internet access, and gave rise to a whole new classification of Internet-linked Amateur "stations": licensed amateurs who were connecting themselves to distant repeaters using only a computer.

The doors opened even wider with *eQSO*, developed by Paul Davies,

MØZPD. Like *iLINK, eQSO* runs on conventional *Windows* PCs, and allows direct PC-based access to remote links. It specifically permits access by non-hams, either in a listen-only mode, or in off-air conferences. *eQSO* remains popular today.

Yaesu (Vertex Standard) entered the world of Amateur Internet linking with a hardware-software product called *WIRES-II*, in 2002. In conjunction with a set of Internet-based servers operated by Yaesu, the product functions similarly to some of the other linking systems, providing a "plug-and-play" solution for hams wishing to set up a link on a *Windows*-based computer.

Following the success of *iLINK*, my own contribution (in mid-2002) was a compatible software package called *EchoLink*. The program was originally designed to offer an alternative look-and-feel and feature set for *iLINK* users, but quickly evolved into a complete system of its own, due to its rapid (and unexpected) rate of acceptance. By early 2004, *EchoLink* had been installed and registered by more than 110,000 licensed hams in 147 countries, and typically carried more than 1,400 repeaters and simplex links and about 700 PC-based users at any given time.

Although Internet linking has been going full-tilt for several years, it's interesting to see that it shows no signs of leveling off. On the contrary, it continues to grow steadily, and may even be accelerating in its rate of acceptance (**Figure 1.2**). It seems that Internet linking has finally come of age!

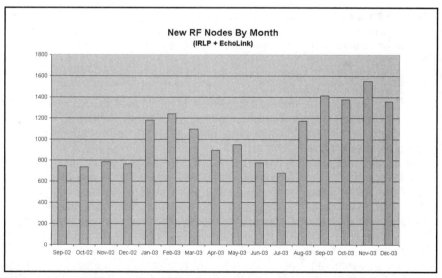

Figure 1.2—Recent growth in *IRLP* and *EchoLink* installations. Each bar represents the number of new nodes joining the system (validations or installations) in the specified month. Although many new nodes are temporary, the data shows that Internet linking continues to gain acceptance rapidly. (Sources: *EchoLink* database and www.irlp.net).

WHAT IS INTERNET LINKING?

Hams have come up with various ways of joining Amateur Radio to the Internet, but *Internet linking*, in the context of this book, refers to using the Internet to connect Amateur Radio stations to each other to exchange voice signals. Since amateur Internet linking uses VoIP to accomplish this feat, Internet linking is sometimes simply called VoIP.

As you know, ham stations take on many different forms, and the ones most commonly used with Internet links are FM repeater stations and simplex stations on the VHF and UHF bands. Some systems extend the definition of a "station" to include "remote base" types of operation, where one end of the link is a licensed amateur sitting in front of a computer rather than a radio.

VHF/UHF FM is a natural mode for Internet-linked stations, since it's geared toward low-power portable and mobile stations, which have the greatest need for widely extended coverage. And for any kind of automatic relay, including Internet links, FM works well because of its good voice quality and positive squelch action. Finally, Internet links are a natural extension to the function of existing FM repeaters, many of which already have sophisticated controllers that provide additional services beyond basic radio relay.

Moore's Law

It took a number of years from the introduction of the first personal computer for the PC to become a common piece of equipment in the household. Now, is seems that most households that have a PC also have one or two *old* PCs. Today's screaming machine is destined to become next year's digital boat anchor, making PCs among the *worst* investments you'll ever make.

You can blame it on a principle known as Moore's Law. Back in 1965, a fellow named Gordon Moore noticed that the number of transistors that could be fit on an integrated circuit was growing exponentially, and he boldly announced that the trend would continue.

Nearly 40 years and seven American presidents later, a lot has happened in the technology world. But Gordon Moore's "law," which states that chip density (and thus computing power) tends to double every couple of years, still holds true.

The good news is that the computer you buy two years from now will be more than twice as powerful as the one you buy today. The bad news is that the computer you just bought today will be only half as powerful as the next one you buy, two years from now.

Software developers are sometimes fond of finishing a project and then saying, "We certainly have Moore's Law working in our favor." Now that you know what Moore's Law is all about, you'll realize that what they're really saying is, "Gee, our software is really slow and poorly designed. But instead of fixing it, if we just sit around and wait for the hardware to improve, it sure will run a lot faster in a couple of years!"

SOFTWARE, SERVICES AND SYSTEMS

The most basic type of Internet link is shown in **Figure 1.3**. At each end of the connection, audio from the receiver is piped into the sound card of a PC, where it is converted to digital packets and transmitted over the Internet to the other end. Then, the data is converted back into sound and fed into the microphone jack of a transmitter. The whole process is reversible, so that the two stations can carry on a conversation.

This kind of set-up might be fine for a permanent, point-to-point link, but the real power of Internet linking is its ability to make *ad hoc* connections to other stations, when and where needed. In order for this to work, at least three new ingredients must be thrown in:

1) Common software, or standard protocols. Each station in the system needs to be running software which is the same, or which is designed to interoperate with others, so that any station can connect to any other and be able to exchange signals.

2) Control. Besides simply exchanging voice signals, there should be some agreed-upon way to establish a new link, and to release it.

3) Directory services. The Internet uses numeric addresses rather than call signs, so there needs to be some way to locate a distant station on the Internet, such as by its call sign or node number.

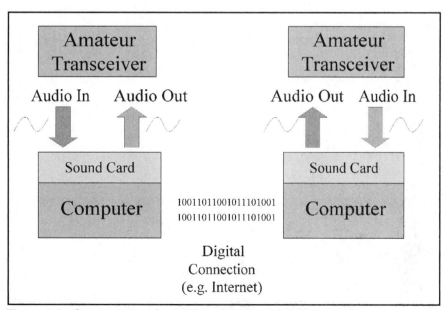

Figure 1.3—Components of a basic point-to-point VoIP system.

4) Security. Since the Internet is a public network, each link needs some efficient way to restrict access, and to identify which station is connecting.

To satisfy these needs, *linking systems* have emerged. Each of these systems is a package that includes software (and sometimes hardware), plus services. Broadly speaking, the software takes care of requirements 1 and 2, and the services take care of requirements 3 and 4.

ABOUT THIS BOOK

This book introduces Internet linking, and describes several of the most widely used systems, with particular attention to *EchoLink* and *IRLP*. It gives some basic advice about how to operate an Internet link, how to plan, set up, and customize your own. It also provides a peek into the innards of these systems, with some background on how VoIP works, and some of the digital magic that goes on behind the scenes.

Internet linking is a relatively new and fast-moving aspect of Amateur Radio, and I won't try to dive deeply into the details of how to set up and configure each individual system. At this level, each system is quite different, and software can change substantially with each new release. Fortunately, plenty of useful documentation is available online. See the Appendix at the end of the book for helpful links.

Chapter 2

Using a VoIP Link

If you're already comfortable with FM simplex and repeater operating procedures, using an Internet link will be an easy transition. For the most part, carrying on a conversation over an Internet link isn't much different than speaking with local stations on the repeater. But as with every Amateur Radio mode, there are a few important guidelines to follow.

MAKING THE CONNECTION

A popular misconception about VoIP linking is that you need a computer to use it. Not at all! In most cases, you can fire up the link using the DTMF pad on your transceiver.

Most systems have a set of standard DTMF (*TouchTone*) codes that can be used to connect to another station, or disconnect. As long as you're in range of the link (or the repeater to which it is linked), and operation by traveling users is welcomed, you can connect to any other Internet-linked station in the world from your transceiver. Before using a VoIP node, check with the node owner (or club) to see what the operating policies are.

With *EchoLink*, *IRLP* and *WIRES-II*, every station on the system is assigned a unique *node number*. Node numbers are four, five or six digits long. If you know the node number of the station you want to connect to, you can usually punch it in directly to initiate a contact. By default, on *EchoLink* and *IRLP,* no special prefix or suffix is required. However, each node owner has the option of customizing this feature.

First, listen to be sure the frequency isn't in use. Then, announce your call sign and your intentions, such as "This is W1XXX, connecting." Let it drop for a moment, then key the rig again, and using the DTMF pad, enter the node number of the station. Drop it again, and wait for an acknowledgement from the system.

If all goes well, you'll hear a voice announcement indicating that you're connected to the remote station over the Internet. If the connection couldn't be made, you'll hear an announcement about that instead. Common reasons for not being able to connect are:

- the node number you entered doesn't exist;
- the remote link (or the local link) isn't up and running; or
- the remote link is already in use and not accepting any more connections.

If the connection succeeds, you've opened up a two-way channel between the local frequency and the remote station. If the remote station is a repeater or a simplex link, you've set up a temporary "wormhole" between two local coverage areas in different parts of the world! During your conversation, it's helpful to visualize the communications path between you and the remote station. The diagram in Figure 1.1 in the previous chapter is a good reference.

This will be familiar territory if you've ever used repeaters that are linked together by phone lines or auxiliary RF links. For the most part, you operate just as you normally would, making short transmissions and giving remote users ample time to reply. The only big difference is that there's an extra delay—for reasons that will be explained later—so it's *very* important to leave extra space between transmissions. You could say that the three most important rules are "pause, listen and pause again."

You: "This is W1XXX connecting." (*pause*)

You: (*DTMF digits:* 1 2 3 4)

Link: "XX1ZZ Connected. Welcome to the XX1ZZ Node, serving Greater Hamburg and Radio Valley."

You: (*pause for 10 seconds...*) "This is W1XXX listening."

The Pause Rule is especially important if you're in a three-way conversation, with two stations on the local repeater and a third station on the remote link. When the other local station turns it over to you, wait a little longer than usual to give another remote station a chance to break in. And the Pause Rule is vital if you're participating in a larger group, such as a traffic net, when stations might need to break in at any time from anywhere. Nothing is more frustrating than connecting to a remote repeater, hearing a conversation in progress, but not being able to get a word in edgewise because the other stations are "picking it up" too quickly.

DISCONNECTING

When the conversation is finished, it's important to disconnect the link, unless someone else wants to start a chat with the same station.

Although there are standard codes for disconnecting—for example, *EchoLink* uses the pound sign (#), and *WIRES-II* uses the string #9999D— the node owner might have assigned special codes instead. Among other things, the repeater itself might have advanced functions that would be inadvertently triggered by entering a certain string of DTMF digits. Before making a connection, be sure you know how to disconnect afterwards!

Table 2.1
EchoLink DTMF Control Functions

Command	Description	Default
Connect	Connects to a station on the Internet, based on its node number.	*num*
Connect by Call	Connects to a station on the Internet, based on its call sign.	**C**+call
Random Node	Selects an available node (of any type) at random, and tries to connect to it.	**00**
Random Link	Selects an available link or repeater (-L or -R) at random, and tries to connect to it.	**01**
Random Conf	Selects a conference server at random, and tries to connect to it.	**02**
Random User	Selects an available single-user station at random, and tries to connect to it.	**03**
RandomFavNode	Selects an available node (of any type) at random from the Favorites List, and tries to connect to it.	**001**
RandomFavLink	Selects an available link or repeater (-L or -R) at random from the Favorites List, and tries to connect to it.	**011**
RandomFavConf	Selects a conference server at random from the Favorites List, and tries to connect to it.	**021**
RandomFavUser	Selects an available single-user station at random from the Favorites List, and tries to connect to it.	**031**
Disconnect	Disconnects the station that is currently connected. If more than one station is connected, disconnects only the most-recently-connected station.	**#**
Disconnect All	Disconnects all stations.	**##**
Reconnect	Re-connects to the station that most recently disconnected.	**09**
Status	Announces the call sign of each station currently connected.	**08**
Play Info	Plays a brief ID message.	*****
Query by Call	Looks up a station by its call sign, and reads back its node number and status.	**07**+*call*+**#**
Query by Node	Looks up a station by its node number, and reads back its call sign and status.	**06**+*num*
Listen-Only On	Inhibits transmission from RF to the Internet.	**0511**
Listen-Only Off	Restores normal transmission from RF to the Internet.	**0510**

OTHER COMMANDS

EchoLink has a special feature that allows visitors to listen to a brief informational message about the link. The standard code for calling this up is the star key (*).

A number of other standard *EchoLink* DTMF control functions are available. **Table 2.1** lists many of these functions, and the default DTMF sequence for each. Again, keep in mind that the node owner may have changed some of these to non-standard sequences.

NUMBER, PLEASE

One of the difficulties with the node numbering system is finding out (or trying to remember) the node number for a particular station. I've tried a few techniques, such as yellow Post-It notes stuck to the dashboard, and driving around with the printed *EchoLink*, *IRLP* and *WIRES-II* node directories—altogether about the size of a city telephone book—but clearly there *must* be a better way.

Perhaps in the future there will be an Internet Linking directory-assistance node, staffed by volunteers, complete with advice about local restaurants and attractions. In the meantime, here are some resources for locating node numbers:

Lists on the Web. Each of the major linking systems has a Web site that includes a complete list of active nodes, with call sign, location, node number and status.

Web search pages. Several sites will produce searchable lists of Internet links that can be sorted several ways, such as by distance from a particular location. Some of these sites will also produce maps showing the geographical position of each link, along with its node number. You might want to print maps of a few areas of interest and keep them in a folder with your mobile station.

Personal lists. As you browse the Web directories, make a note of node numbers you're likely to be interested in using in the future, and (in particular) the numbers of other nodes near you. You might find that the links you use most often are those within 100 miles of your station.

On-air functions. *EchoLink*, in particular, has a feature that allows you to connect to a station by entering its call sign (or part of its call sign) using the DTMF keypad. It uses a system where each letter and number is designated by pressing two DTMF digits. See the *EchoLink* documentation for details.

Shortcut commands. The node owner may have set up certain shortcut DTMF sequences for commonly used nodes, perhaps only one or two digits long.

AVRS. Although not yet in widespread use, there is a feature of the APRS network called AVRS, or Automatic Voice Reporting System. This system allows an Internet link to send a local beacon to announce its presence and status to mobile stations nearby. APRS rigs with receive-and-display capability, such as the Kenwood TM-D700, will decode this information and display it on the rig's front panel.

COMMON COURTESY

A repeater is very much a shared resource; and, in a sense, so is a simplex frequency. If you use a local repeater or simplex link for Internet linking, please be considerate. Here are some guidelines to follow:

After connecting to another station, wait 15 seconds to determine whether there's already a conversation in progress on the remote frequency. This is also important when connecting to a conference server or reflector.

If you used a DTMF command to establish a connection to another station, it's your responsibility to drop the connection at the end of the chat, unless another local station wants to pick it up.

Conference servers or reflectors are great for roundtable conversations, but not a good choice for extended one-on-one conversations. If you run into an old friend on a conference server and want to carry on a 30-minute exchange, set up a direct connection instead.

When linked to another station, keep all transmissions short, and leave plenty of extra space between transmissions to allow link repeaters' timers to reset. The extra space also gives others a chance to jump in and disconnect, if desired.

In some situations (particularly on reflectors and conferences), it's important to key the mic for one second before you begin talking. This will ensure that all receivers tuned to link output frequencies have a chance to "open up" before the audio begins. If a tone-squelched receiver takes 200 ms to respond, a chain of *three* tone-squelched receivers takes more than half a second.

Although operating procedures are much like VHF-FM, conversations are often more like HF-SSB. The station you're in contact with might be 12 time zones away, in the opposite season, and not sharing the same first language with you. Remember this, even if some of the other stations in the roundtable are locals. When announcing your station location, avoid saying something like "five miles south of the Park Street exit on Highway 42." The locals might know what you mean, but to a distant station, it's meaningless.

On *EchoLink*, avoid using remote nodes as if they were conference servers. For example, if you connect to W1XXX-R and find no one on frequency, but then get involved in a conversation with someone else who connects to W1XXX-R, drop the W1XXX-R connection and move the chat to a direct connection. Otherwise, you're tying up the W1XXX/R frequency for no good reason.

Don't leave a repeater-to-repeater link connected unless the stations using the repeater are aware that the link is active. For example, don't leave the link up and running for an extended period, unless prior arrangements have been made between the repeater clubs. Otherwise, stations having a conversation on one repeater might not be aware that they're working through another repeater at the same time.

If you're planning to use an Internet link for the first time, check with a local station first to see if there are any special rules or conventions for using the node. If you are planning a cross-country trip and want to use Internet links along the way, you might want to contact each node owner in advance to introduce yourself and learn about how the link is operated.

Keep in mind that the primary purpose of the repeater is to extend the range of mobile and portable stations, and that Internet linking is secondary. Drop the Internet link if it is impeding local communications in any way. This is particularly important since a local station might need to break in at any time with emergency or priority traffic.

LINKING FROM THE DESKTOP

Some of the popular Amateur Radio VoIP systems also have a mode that allows licensed hams to make an Internet voice connection directly from their desktop (or laptop) PC, using the PC's microphone and speakers. This is a good solution for a single, fixed user, since it requires no RF link at the originating end, and thus uses no additional equipment or spectrum space.

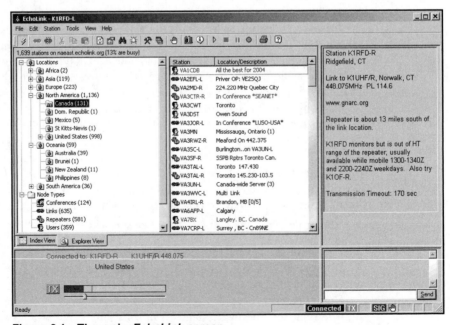

Figure 2.1—The main *EchoLink* screen.

In this mode, you are shown a list of all available stations, from which you can make a selection and click to connect. Stations are generally listed with their call sign and location (or description). You can usually also exchange text messages with other single-user stations.

Figure 2.1 shows the main screen that *EchoLink* displays while it's running. The list of stations at the center of the screen is organized by location, using folders and sub-folders similar to *Windows Explorer*. The space bar works like a locking push-to-talk switch—tap once to begin transmitting, tap again to stop transmitting. The horizontal bar graph near the bottom is an audio-level meter that displays both transmitted and received audio levels. Other systems have similar screens and functions in this mode.

A convention adopted by *EchoLink* and *eQSO* is to identify RF nodes with a call sign suffix, either -L or -R, and single-user, PC-based nodes with no suffix. The -L suffix indicates that the node is a simplex link, and -R indicates a link to a repeater. On *EchoLink*, even single-user nodes have an assigned node number, so they, too, can be reached via DTMF commands from mobile users working through a distant link.

If you are running a Macintosh computer with the *OS X* operating system, you can also connect to *EchoLink* nodes using a program called *EchoMac*, developed by Steven Palm, N9YTY. *EchoMac* is an open-source VoIP package designed to be fully compatible with *EchoLink*, fulfilling the need for desktop Internet linking for Mac users. It can be downloaded from **www.dogparksoftware.com**. *EchoMac* is based partly on a project called *EchoLinux*, spearheaded by Jeff Pierce, WD4NMQ, which brings an *EchoLink*-compatible client to the *Linux* platform.

Chapter 3

Conference Servers, Reflectors and Nets

We often take for granted one of the useful aspects of radio communication: the fact that one transmission can be picked up by more than one receiver. Roundtables and traffic nets are a mainstay of ham activity. One person makes a transmission, and everyone else listening on the frequency hears it. Imagine how different things would be if every message had to be one-to-one, and sent separately to each station participating in a net. Aside from being extremely repetitive and time-consuming, it would be a tremendous waste of bandwidth, and be a huge obstacle to effective public service communications. After all, part of what makes Amateur Radio so useful for disaster communications, compared to cell phones, is its ability to get everyone tuned to the same frequency to hear the same message.

But the Internet is quite different. Virtually all communication over the Internet is point-to-point. The TCP protocol, used by most Internet traffic, is strictly one-to-one; for each message, there is just one sender and one recipient. The UDP protocol, commonly used by VoIP systems, usually has only one sender and one recipient as well. Although UDP does have provisions for *multicasting*—sending a single message to more than one recipient—most Internet providers do not support it. If you have a message that needs to be "heard" by more than one recipient, it'll have to be sent separately to each one, somewhere along the line.

On the surface, this looks like a real showstopper for Amateur Radio VoIP systems. Does this mean that every VoIP conversation must be one-to-one? Are roundtables and traffic nets just impossible over Internet links?

Fortunately, there's a solution. A specially designed software package, called a *conference server, conference bridge* or *reflector*, makes one-to-many communications possible over the Internet. As the name implies, a reflector takes in a message—in this case, a digitized voice transmission—and spits it right back out again. What makes it useful is that it can "spit" in many directions at once. The reflector keeps a running list of every station that wants to receive a copy of each message, and each time a message comes in, it sends a copy to everyone on the list, except for the sender (**Figure 3.1**). This way, every station that is connected to the reflector can hear what every other station is saying.

While this might sound horribly inefficient (and in some ways it is), it all happens in the blink of an eye, and quite automatically. Stations connected to the reflector hear every other station speaking in turn, just like an on-air roundtable, and might easily forget all the hard work that's going on behind the scenes.

Figure 3.1—A conference server sends a copy of each packet it receives to every other participating node. The conference server needs extra upstream Internet bandwidth, but the participating nodes do not.

One of the downsides, however, is that reflectors and conference servers use a lot of Internet bandwidth. If 10 stations are connected to the reflector, every packet of data received must be re-sent separately to each of the other nine stations. For this to work, the reflector must have an Internet connection that can easily handle uploading nine times the normal bandwidth of a VoIP connection. Because of this, conference servers and reflectors are usually connected to the Internet using big "pipes," such as OC-3 connections, which can accommodate the higher data rate.

Keep in mind that the reflector is doing all of the heavy lifting here. From each individual station's point of view, it's a one-to-one connection between the station and the reflector. Although messages (i.e., voices) from many different stations are being heard, they're all being relayed from a single point, namely the reflector. This means that a station participating in a roundtable conversation on a reflector doesn't have any additional Internet bandwidth requirements of its own.

In theory, a whole network of reflectors or conference servers could be interconnected to accommodate a very large conference, with hundreds of participants. The advantage to doing it this way, instead of using just one giant conference server, is that it distributes the Internet bandwidth requirements among several connections, instead of just one (**Figure 3.2**). Voice packets from stations connected to Reflector 1 are relayed to Reflector 2, where they are re-sent to each of Reflector 2's participants. If Reflector 1 has fifty stations connected, and Reflector 2 has 50 stations connected, each reflector needs to send only 50 copies of each message to serve all 99 recipients. In practice, however, this is rarely necessary, since conferences of that size can become unwieldy.

On *IRLP*, reflectors are a prime meeting place for VoIP connections. There are currently about 20 reflectors available on *IRLP*. Each has a four-digit node number beginning with 9, such as 9200. The reflectors are generally named after their geographical location: the Alaska Reflector, the Indiana Reflector. Many of the reflectors support multiple *channels,* each of which can carry a completely separate conversation. To connect to a particular channel on a reflector, change the last digit of the node number. For example, to connect to Channel 4 on Reflector 9200, connect to node number 9204. A special reflector, called the "echo reflector," records and plays back each individual station's audio for testing and adjustment. The echo reflector is node 9990. If you are setting up a brand new *IRLP* node, or moving it to different hardware, your first stop should be Node 9990 to be sure everything's up to snuff.

Recall that *IRLP* supports either of two different codecs: GSM and ADPCM. All *IRLP* reflectors support ADPCM, but by convention, GSM connections are usually supported only on channels 8 and 9 of multi-channel reflectors.

EchoLink also supports conferencing, in a similar fashion, but with dif-

Figure 3.2—Two or more conference servers, when linked together, can serve a large number of nodes without requiring lots of upstream bandwidth at any single site. In this example, five stations are in the roundtable, but no single conference server is "feeding" more than three.

ferent nomenclature. *EchoLink* reflectors are called conference servers, and have short, alphanumeric names that begin and end with an asterisk, such as *WX_TALK*. *EchoLink* does not reserve any specific range of node numbers for conference servers, so numbers can be four, five or six digits in length. You'll typically find about 100 *EchoLink* conference servers online, many of which are devoted to a particular topic or language. Some of the conference servers are interconnected as described previously. *EchoLink* conference servers run on an open-source package called *theBridge*, developed by Skip Hansen, WB6YMH, which runs on any of several different operating systems, including *Windows* and *Linux*.

An interesting feature of *EchoLink* is that the *EchoLink* software itself supports conferencing, so each *EchoLink* node can host its own mini-conference, bandwidth permitting. One nice thing about this feature is that two *EchoLink* stations that are in a one-to-one chat with each other can "conference in" a third station without having to move the QSO to a conference server. Another benefit is that any number of stations can remain connected to an *EchoLink* node, in order to monitor it, without blocking out others from connecting. It's also slightly more efficient (in terms of Internet bandwidth) than using a conference server, since local RF users participate in the conference directly, without requiring an additional Internet path.

WIRES-II and *eQSO*, described in the next chapter, have conferencing features as well. *WIRES-II* supports a Round Table mode, and *eQSO* is actually built entirely around the concept of conference rooms.

THOSE BLEEPING BLEEPS

When many stations are participating in the same conference, it's important that each node exercises good engineering discipline (and good operating practices). Part of this is making sure that the node doesn't transmit repeater IDs, courtesy tones and other assorted noises. Imagine the cacophony of 50 repeater links connected to the same reflector, each announcing the call sign, date, time and temperature every six minutes, even though no one is actually in a conversation!

This isn't usually a problem if the link equipment is co-located with the repeater. By picking off the repeater receiver's audio directly, instead of the audio coming out of the controller, none of these extra noises are heard over the Internet link.

But it's more of a challenge if the VoIP link is located at someone's station, away from the repeater. Here, the only source of signal is the *output* of the repeater, rather than the *input*, so suppressing the sounds generated by the controller is much more difficult.

There are four common solutions:

The first is to simply eliminate these sounds from the repeater altogether, and shorten the "hang time" to almost nil. Although this is usually easy to do, it tends to intrude into the repeater's normal behavior, and thus might not be too popular with repeater users who have no interest in the Internet link.

Another solution is to set up a second RF path between the repeater site and the node site. Typically, a UHF auxiliary link transmitter is set up at the repeater site, beaming the main receiver's audio directly to a matching UHF receiver at the node site. (These UHF rigs could also be transceivers, and used to carry the link audio in both directions, but it's not essential.) What makes this option attractive is that the node is working with the true audio path from the repeater's receiver, just as if it was co-located with the repeater.

The third solution is to try to suppress these extraneous signals within the linking software (or hardware) itself. *EchoLink*, for example, has a "Smart VOX" feature that will prevent noise bursts—such as squelch tails and courtesy tones—from triggering the VOX and being heard over the link. (This is described in more detail in Chapter 7.) But this is not completely effective if the repeater transmits other signals, such as a CW or voice ID, which do not resemble noise bursts.

The fourth (and probably best) solution is to use a sub-audible tone, generated by the repeater, to indicate the presence of a signal at the repeater's input. The tone generator is switched on and off by the COS signal from the repeater's receiver. This way, a remote receiver, such as the link radio, can use tone squelch (also called CTCSS, or PL) to determine whether the repeater is actually receiving a signal.

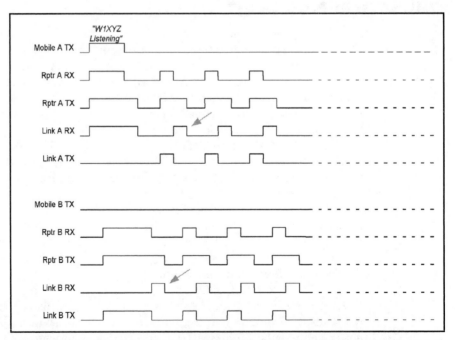

Figure 3.3—Timing diagram of The Kerchunk Of Death. With Link A and Link B both improperly adjusted, W1XYZ's innocent ID sets in motion a vicious cycle of phantom transmissions, in which the two repeaters keep bringing each other up. The root of the problem is that both Link A and Link B are sending their own "tails" back over the Internet (gray arrows).

This is an excellent approach, since it usually requires no additional equipment. Many repeaters, whether or not they use CTCSS on their *inputs*, already have a CTCSS encoder available, so it's just a matter of wiring its control line to the receiver's COS output. Sophisticated repeater control boards might even support making such a "connection" in software. Making such a change is usually completely transparent to normal repeater users, who are unlikely to be using tone squelch in their receivers. The node owner then just needs to enable the tone-squelch feature of his link transceiver and call it a day.

Of course, this doesn't *completely* eliminate the sound of repeater CW IDs, since the node is still using the repeater's output audio path, rather than its input receiver's audio. So a CW ID would still be heard underneath a station using a repeater, if the ID happened to come on during someone's transmission. But we will have achieved our goal of preventing the repeater's own ancillary signals from keying up the link when no one is actually speaking.

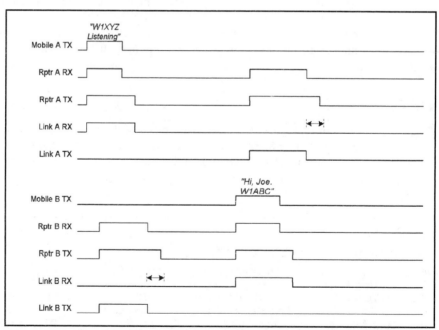

Figure 3.4—With the addition of an "anti-thump" (or "pulseback") timer at both ends (arrows), the problem is solved, and W1XYZ and W1ABC can enjoy a conversation. The timer begins at the moment the link PTT is dropped. During this time, the link receiver's COS is ignored. However, if the anti-thump timer is too long (more than a second or so), it tends to interfere with normal activity by clipping the beginning of each transmission.

Suppressing these ancillary signals is a good idea for *any* node, even one that never connects to a conference server. One situation that's especially important to avoid is ping-ponging between linked repeaters (**Figures 3.3 and 3.4**). If, at both ends of the Internet connection, the repeater's courtesy tone or squelch tail triggers a VOX-operated node, the two nodes will exchange "kerchunks" repeatedly until someone steps in and breaks the vicious cycle.

NODE BLOCKING

To encourage the adoption of good engineering practices, and to prevent unintentional interference to others, owners of *IRLP* reflectors (and some *EchoLink* conference servers) enforce the rule that no extraneous repeater IDs, courtesy tones and the like may be sent to the reflector. Nodes that do send these signals can be temporarily *blocked* from using the reflector, until the problem is corrected.

A listing on the **www.irlp.net** Web site shows the status of blocked nodes for each reflector. If you're an *IRLP* node owner and you find that your node is unable to connect to certain reflectors, check this list to see if your node has been blocked. (Chances are, you will have already received a polite e-mail from the reflector owner, reminding you to double-check your system.)

NETS

Conference servers and reflectors are a natural fit for scheduled nets. Just as with FM repeater and HF SSB nets, Internet linking nets typically have a scheduled place and time, a net control station and check-ins. **Table 3.1** lists a few examples.

Table 3.1

A Sampling of Internet-Linked Nets

Name	Time (winter UTC)	System	Node
EchoLink Help Forum	Thursday, 0200	EchoLink	6427
IRLP Int'l YL Net	1st/3rd Tues, 0100	IRLP	9000
EchoLink Tech Net	2nd Friday, 0200	EchoLink	6427
IRLP SKYWARN Net	Sunday, 0000	IRLP	9210
Visually Challenged Net	Tuesday, 2300	IRLP	9608
IRLP Swap Net	Friday, 0100	IRLP	9255
Handi-Ham Net	Tuesday, 0100	EchoLink	39980
Traders Swap & Shop Net	Tuesday, 0200	EchoLink	6427
Cleveland QCWA Chapter	Thursday, 0100	EchoLink	79637

The main difference between net procedure and normal conference-server procedure is that instead of working as a roundtable, stations are usually called upon to make transmissions by a net control station. As with other amateur nets, a good net control operator is vital to keeping the net activities organized and the communications focused on the task or topic at hand. This is particularly important in the Internet linking world, where every connected station hears every transmission, and only one station can be heard at a time. Timing issues prevent stations from "breaking in" to be recognized, unless called upon by a net control. Nets can easily have more than 100 participating links, each serving a coverage area that could have dozens of stations tuned in.

Rod Templeton, VE7RJT, keeps track of *IRLP* nets and manages a Web page with dates, times and details. For the latest list, visit **www.irlp.net**. Topics range from local radio club gatherings to specialized modes (like SSTV) to swap meets. Each of these nets meets on one of the *IRLP* reflectors around the world.

EchoLink nets typically meet on conference servers, but can also be organized on nodes that are equipped for conferencing. The latter is a good choice for setting up a net where most of the participants are in range of a local repeater (such as a radio club net), but a few are checking in from the distant corners of the globe. Organizations such as Handi-Hams, local Quarter Century Wireless Association chapters and youth groups all have regularly scheduled nets on *EchoLink*. Help nets, "tech" nets and swap nets are held every week on some of the busier conference servers. Check the Calendar in the *EchoLink Yahoo!* group for schedules of some of these nets. Net announcements are sometimes posted in the *EchoLink* node description lines, and often also on the Internet, and retrievable via a Web search.

One interesting feature of an *EchoLink* net is that you can participate directly from your computer, and thus have the benefit of seeing a dynamic list of the other net participants. This also makes the net control operator's job easier, since he or she can see nodes as they come and go, without having to do a general call for check-ins. For example, if W1XYZ-R appears in the list, the net control can make a directed call such as "Anyone on the W1XYZ repeater, please check in now." And, of course, if K6XYZ checks in directly from a PC, he can be recognized specifically.

Internet linking is still gaining acceptance by public service and emergency communications groups, and this trend is likely to continue. A natural way to gain familiarity with Internet linking and its role in emergency communications is to invite linked stations to check in to your local monthly (or weekly) ARES net. Or, if your ARES net meets on a local repeater, set up an Internet link between your repeater and that of another group nearby. If you do, be sure that your net control operator is familiar with Internet linking procedures, to ensure the net runs smoothly.

Chapter 4

Other Linking Systems

WIRES-II

Yaesu (Vertex Standard) has the distinction of being the only commercial Amateur Radio equipment manufacturer (to date) to offer a complete hardware/software package for Internet voice linking. Their product is called *WIRES-II*, which is an acronym for Wide-Coverage Internet Repeater Enhancement System.

The package includes a specialized interface box (called the HRI-100, **Figure 4.1**) that connects your rig to your PC, and a *Windows*-based software package that goes along with it. New users must register by sending a registration form by mail to Yaesu; after processing the request, Yaesu will reply by mail with an ID number that must be entered into the software to activate it. This becomes your node's four-digit identifier.

Yaesu hasn't openly documented the technology behind *WIRES-II*, but it appears to be similar in principle to the other VoIP linking systems described in this book. The heart of the system is an Internet-based server system that Yaesu operates, and into which all registered *WIRES-II* stations connect. Once connected to the server, the software displays a sorted list of all other active stations on the network. Connections can be established either by keyboard or mouse commands at the PC, or by sending DTMF signals through the link radio.

Unique to *WIRES-II* are the concepts of a "Sister Radio Group" (SRG) and a "Friends' Radio Group" (FRG). A given *WIRES-II* station can operate in either mode. In SRG mode, up to ten repeaters and/or home stations may join to form a Sister Radio Group for closed-network operations. This is said to be ideal for emergency, school or sister-city groups. In FRG mode, any other *WIRES-II* station (anywhere in the world) can be contacted, as long as it, too, is operating in FRG mode.

Figure 4.1—The HRI-100 in service at K1RFD.

The SRG mode sets up what is essentially a private network; only a small number of other designated *WIRES-II* stations can be a part of it. Besides security and privacy, one benefit of an SRG (and the magic number ten) is that any other station in the group can be called by pressing a single DTMF digit. In FRG mode, stations are accessed using six-digit DTMF codes.

SRG (**Figure 4.2**) sports an interesting feature, particularly for emergency communications. The *WIRES-II* software can run in either the "Lock" mode or the "Unlock" mode. In the Lock mode, a single DTMF digit calls another station in the group, and the connection remains established until it's dropped, or times out. But in the Unlock mode, the DTMF digit is sent at the beginning of *each* transmission. This allows a mobile or portable station to selectively send a single message to a single *WIRES-II* node, sort of like the push-to-talk bar on an intercom. This way, a group of repeaters in nearby cities can be continuously linked with *WIRES*, but only certain *transmissions* are exchanged over the Internet, leaving most of the repeater activity local. This might be ideal for groups of busy repeaters that don't want to be part of a 24-hour-a-day conference, yet still want to exchange messages occasionally.

In FRG mode (**Figure 4.3**), a portable or mobile station tuned to a *WIRES-*

Calling SRG Node 1
Press the DTMF [1] key while transmitting, to call SRG Node "1" within your SRG Group.

Calling SRG Node 0
Press the DTMF [0] key while transmitting, to call SRG Node "0" within your SRG Group.

SRG3

SRG4

SRG2

SRG5

(#1101D)
SRG0

Internet
Connection

(#1102D)
SRG1

HRI-100   PC

PC   HRI-100

In SRG mode, linked staions communicate via the internet on a peer-to-peer basis.

SRG List
SRG 0 1101
SRG 1 1102
SRG 2 5100
SRG 3 5101
SRG 4 5102
SRG 5 5103
SRG 6 5104
SRG 7 5105
SRG 8 5106
SRG 9 5107
SRG 9 5108
SRG 9 5109

SRG List
SRG 0 1101
SRG 1 1102
SRG 2 5100
SRG 3 5101
SRG 4 5102
SRG 5 5103
SRG 6 5104
SRG 7 5105
SRG 8 5106
SRG 9 5107
SRG 9 5108
SRG 9 5109

SRG6

SRG8

SRG7

SRG9

Calling All SRG Nodes
To call all nodes in your SRG Group press the DTMF [A] key while transmitting.

Figure 4.2—The *WIRES-II* SRG system diagram. (*Vertex Standard*)

II link can connect to any other FRG node by pressing the DTMF pound-sign (#), followed by the four-digit node number, followed by the letter D. To disconnect, send either #9999D or #99999.

As with other linking systems, the PC and interface box can be located either at a repeater site, or at any convenient off-site location using a link transceiver. A special interface cable is provided with stripped and tinned leads to connect the interface box to the audio input, audio output, and COS output of either a link transceiver or a repeater. (Yaesu even offers pre-made cables for some of its own FM rigs.) Miniature phone jacks and patch cords make the audio connections to the PC's sound card, and a serial interface cable goes between the PC's COM port and the *WIRES-II* interface box, to handle control functions such as PTT.

Either a dial-up or a broadband Internet connection can be used. In fact, the *WIRES-II* software can be set up to automatically dial into an ISP when it starts, and automatically re-dial if the connection is ever dropped. **Figure 4.4** shows the *WIRES-II* screen as it appears on the host PC.

Although the documentation doesn't specifically say it, it certainly seems that the PC used for a *WIRES-II* station should be dedicated to the task—

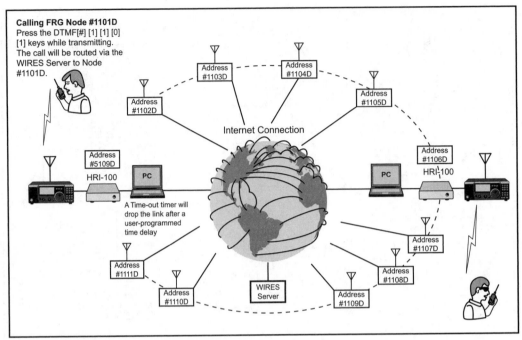

Figure 4.3—The *WIRES-II* FRG system diagram. (*Vertex Standard*)

don't use your home-office machine. The manual states that a large number of TCP/IP ports must be "opened" to the Internet (ten thousand, in fact!), and that Yaesu will, from time to time, log in to your PC over the Internet to do necessary software updates. The minimum PC system requirements are a 300-MHz Celeron processor and 64 MB RAM.

Several updates to the software have been released since *WIRES-II* was first introduced, each with significant new features. Product owners are sent an e-mail notification when a new release is available, and the new software can be downloaded from the *WIRES-II* Web site. The latest version supports features such as text chat and a Round Table QSO mode, similar to the conferencing mode of other programs. It also allows a picture (such as a QSL card) to be exchanged between nodes.

WIRES-II is relatively new on the scene, and most of its growth so far appears to have been in Japan and the US. In early 2004, approximately 600 stations worldwide were listed as registered with *WIRES*. Of these, about 73% were in Japan, and about 17% were in the United States.

For more information about *WIRES-II* in English, see **www.vxstd.com/ en/wiresinfo-en**.

Figure 4.4—A screen snapshot of the *WIRES-II* software.

EQSO

For several years, many *Windows* users have enjoyed an Internet linking program called *eQSO*. Paul Davies, MØZPD, developed *eQSO*.

eQSO is actually a family of several different programs, for different purposes. PC Client software lets users connect to the system using the keyboard, microphone and speaker of their PC. RF Gateway software supports interconnecting the PC with an FM transceiver or repeater, to operate a simplex or repeater link. Server software runs a conference server, in which any number of rooms can be created. Conference servers allow multiple *eQSO* stations to be connected to each other in a single conversation. Conference servers are roughly equivalent to *reflectors* in *IRLP*, and rooms are analogous to *IRLP* reflector *channels*.

The RF Gateway software (**Figure 4.5**) works with several different types of PC-to-rig interfaces, including general-purpose sound card interfaces and Internet Linking boards.

One significant difference between *eQSO* and other VoIP systems is that

Figure 4.5—A view of the *eQSO* RF Gateway software in action.

all communication occurs in conference rooms. In other words, stations do not connect to each other to communicate; instead, they each connect to a common conference room. Although perhaps less efficient for one-to-one QSOs, one interesting benefit of this arrangement is that *eQSO* is somewhat more "firewall friendly" than other systems. Rather than accepting *inbound* UDP connections from the Internet, as other systems do, all *eQSO* users establish *outbound* TCP connections to the conference server when they want to chew the rag. This simplifies firewall configuration (except at the conference server itself), since most home/office firewalls will allow outbound TCP connections without special configuration, yet usually require custom setup to support inbound connections. What's more, many offices and other institutions don't allow inbound Internet connections, for security reasons.

The downside is that TCP is generally less efficient than UDP for doing voice communication over the Internet, for a given payload. It also tends to introduce wider gaps in the audio when the Internet path becomes congested, and is more sensitive to latency, such as over satellite links. But over a clear, reliable connection, the results can still be excellent.

It's been said that *eQSO*'s security is based on the honor system. There is no call sign validation process; new users are simply asked to use their own, valid call sign when running the program. In fact, there is no stipulation that only licensed amateurs may have access to *eQSO*. The author of the program has made provisions for interested non-hams (SWLs) to use the program, on the condition that they not transmit in conference rooms that might contain on-air links. SWLs are free to listen in these rooms, but two-way communication is restricted to off-air conference rooms. SWLs are asked to create an identifier in lieu of a call sign, such as SWL-TOM, or SWL-12345.

Administrators of *eQSO* servers do have the ability to control access by "muting," "kicking" or "banning" users that do not adhere to the operating guidelines.

In early 2004, about 100 part-time and full-time RF gateways were listed on the *eQSO* Web site.

Since the client and server software are both freely available, it's possible to use *eQSO* to set up an independent, dedicated linking system of your own. With your own dedicated *eQSO* server, you have the option of permitting access only to a limited number of stations—such as RF links to a family of repeaters owned by your club—or "advertising" its presence to the ham community at large. The disadvantage, of course, is that the system would be unable to communicate with stations outside of the private group.

For more information about *eQSO*, see **www.eqso.com**.

SPEAK FREELY

Although not a linking system per se, amateurs might find plenty of good uses for *Speak Freely*, an open-source VoIP package available for both *Windows* and *Unix*.

The program's name was inspired by its ability to make "telephone calls," computer-to-computer, over the Internet, free of charge. It provides the essentials for setting up a VoIP connection, without some of the value-added features that a full-blown linking system provides, such as dynamic addressing and centralized security. It might be worth a look if you're considering a permanent, point-to-point Internet link, such as a dedicated inter-city repeater hookup. Since the source code is freely available, it's a prime candidate for a custom implementation if you (or someone you know) has skills in the *C* programming language.

The program was maintained for many years by John Walker, the original developer, and now can be found on the SourceForge Web site. The *Windows* version is at **sourceforge.net/projects/speak-freely-w/**, and the *Unix* version at **sourceforge.net/projects/speak-freely-u**. A variation on the *Unix* version, in fact, is the "engine" inside *IRLP*.

Chapter 5

Setting Up Your Own Node

We've already pointed out that thousands of hams around the world have used systems such as *IRLP* and *EchoLink* without ever laying hands on a computer. Most of the major systems allow portable and mobile users to connect and disconnect the link using DTMF commands, so Internet linking is truly a two-way experience for mobile and portable stations.

But whether it's hands-on or at a distance, it always requires a computer-based link, somewhere along the way. If you live in an area not already served by a link, consider setting one up yourself! You might find that you already have most of the needed equipment, and the software is easy to get and easy to set up.

COMPONENTS OF AN INTERNET LINK

The basic components of an RF Internet link are a link transceiver, a computer, an Internet connection, linking software and a linking interface.

Link transceiver: Although virtually any VHF/UHF FM transceiver can be used, consider using commercial-grade equipment for better reliability. For an *IRLP* node, the transceiver must have a "busy" or COS pin that indicates (externally) when the squelch is open. This can also be used with *EchoLink*, or VOX control can be used instead.

Computer: Just about any Pentium-based personal computer can be used for either *EchoLink* or *IRLP*. For *IRLP*, the minimum requirement is a Pentium-I CPU, at least 32 MB of RAM, a parallel (printer) port and a Sound Blaster sound card. All of the necessary system software is provided on the *IRLP* installation disk.

For *EchoLink*, the system requirements are similar, except that a serial (COM) port is used instead of a parallel port, and a copy of Microsoft *Windows* is required.

Internet connection: Although a dial-up Internet connection can be used with either *IRLP* or *EchoLink*, a "broadband" connection is strongly preferred, particularly for *IRLP*. Most DSL and cable-modem systems will work fine. There is no need to have a *static* (fixed) IP address.

Linking software: *EchoLink* runs on any 32-bit version of *Windows*, and the *EchoLink* software can be downloaded from the *EchoLink* Web site.

IRLP runs on the *Linux* operating system, which is available (for download) free of charge. In fact, a special distribution of *Linux* is provided on the *IRLP* installation disk. The *IRLP* installation CD comes as part of the *IRLP* start-up kit, which can be ordered online at the *IRLP* Web site.

Linking interface: All *IRLP* nodes use a custom-designed interface circuit that is provided by *IRLP*, as part of the start-up kit. This small circuit board can be mounted inside the PC, or in a separate enclosure. The board connects to the link transceiver, a 12-V power supply and the parallel port of the PC. When mounted inside the PC, the PC's own power supply powers the board.

EchoLink works with any of several different types of linking interfaces, including some specifically designed for *EchoLink*, and others designed for HF digital modes such as PSK31. The interface connects to the computer's serial port. Some interfaces require no external power; others use an external 12-V dc supply. Linking interfaces are described in more detail later in this chapter.

PLAN YOUR SYSTEM

First, determine whether there's a *need* for a new *IRLP* or *EchoLink* node in your area. If there are already several simplex or repeater gateways for Internet linking, you might find that supporting an existing system is the best way to contribute. But if not, this is a great opportunity to expand the communications capabilities for mobile and portable stations in your area. Someone should do it, so why not you?

THE SITE

Second, decide whether the new node will be a simplex gateway, or a link to a local repeater. Naturally, a simplex gateway should be set up on a tall building, tower or hilltop, to provide good simplex coverage. A repeater gateway, on the other hand, can be set up virtually anywhere there's an Internet connection and a good "shot" to the local repeater. Or, it can be placed at the repeater site itself. Either way, you *must* obtain the permission (and blessing) of the group or club that operates the repeater. The link will become a natural extension of the repeater, so it makes sense that it should be operated by an active member of the club that runs the repeater, or the trustee himself or herself, even if the link won't be set up at the repeater site.

If you're considering a simplex gateway, check with the local frequency coordination committee to see what frequencies (if any) have been set aside for Internet linking. Particularly if you live in a well-populated part of the world, you might want to avoid using popular "calling frequencies" for your link.

OPERATING POLICIES

Every Internet voice gateway should have an operating policy. The policy should address what times of day the link will be up and running, who its control operator(s) will be, how it will be controlled, and so forth. If you're setting up a simplex link from your own station, the policy could be as simple as "I'll be the control op, the link will be open to all amateurs, and it will be available 24 hours a day". But if you're planning to link to a repeater, particularly one owned and operated by a club, it makes sense to work with the club (or its repeater committee) to come up with a suitable policy. It need not be written down as a formal document, but it should at least be agreed upon in advance.

The purpose of the policy is to ensure that the link is being used to its best advantage, without interfering with normal use of the frequency, and without violating radio regulations in your country (such as FCC rules in the US). It also helps ensure that the link is providing the emergency communications or public-service benefit it is intended for.

If you are working with a club or a club's repeater committee, a good first step is to offer to do a presentation at the next club meeting on the general topic of Internet linking, with some details on how each of the major linking systems work. A live demo featuring an Internet-linked conversation would be a plus. Be prepared to answer plenty of questions; experience has shown that many hams are aware of Internet linking, but have formed opinions on it (pro or con) based on incomplete, inaccurate, or outdated information. Your focus should be on how the proposed Internet link will benefit the club, the club's repeater and the amateur service in general.

Here are some common objections that might be raised:

"If we hook up our repeater to the Internet, won't that bring in all sorts of unlicensed non-hams?"

There is sometimes a tendency to think of the Internet as a mysterious, lawless jungle, with teenaged hackers "hiding behind keyboards" in darkened basements. In fact, it is simply a global communications medium, which can be made as secure (or insecure) as software and operating policies dictate. And it is potentially much more secure than Amateur Radio itself; Internet communications can be authenticated, traced, and controlled far more efficiently and effectively than RF communications. It all comes down to the security mechanisms of the linking systems themselves, which are discussed in detail later in this book. No security system is perfect, but still, you're likely to find that the greatest risk of striking up a conversation with a non-ham is speaking with someone who had just picked up a handheld transceiver at a local hamfest.

"How could an Internet link possibly help in an emergency? All of the phone lines will be down, so the Internet will be useless."

Without a doubt, emergency-powered radio equipment is the vital link in and out of a disaster area when phone lines go down. But that doesn't mean that Internet linking is useless in an emergency. Health and welfare traffic travels far beyond the affected area, and often, Internet access is still available very close to the scene of a disaster. Linking systems have already played an important role in the aftermath of natural disasters such as hurricanes, even when Internet access had been cut off to many parts of the affected area.

"Our repeater is busy enough as it is. Adding an Internet link will just tie it up even more."

This is a valid concern that should be addressed. Often, the best choice for an Internet linked repeater is one that has good coverage, but relatively light use. Sometimes, however, operating the link only during non-peak periods can solve this problem.

"This all sounds fine, but it's not legal."

This is mostly a matter of operating policy and practices. In most countries, Internet linking is legal if the links are operated in a legal manner. Chapter 9 of this book explores this issue.

"This isn't ham radio!"

Whether or not Internet linking qualifies as part of Amateur Radio is bound to fuel many lengthy philosophical discussions, one of which you'll find in Chapter 10. (Undoubtedly, philosophical discussions are a *vital* part of Amateur Radio!) All other things being equal, however, it is hard to dispute the idea that a repeater with an Internet link is more useful than one without.

As the next step, try to gather answers to the following questions, to form a first draft of the operating policy. At this level of detail, it might be best to discuss these issues in a smaller group, such as the repeater committee or the repeater trustee:

1. Should the link be available 24 hours a day, 7 days a week, or are there certain times when the link should be disabled (or enabled)? If the

repeater is a busy one, you might want to shut down the link during morning and afternoon drive times, for example. *IRLP* and *EchoLink* both can do this automatically with the use of simple scripts. You could start by running the link full-time, and then see if it's necessary to cut back on its operating hours.

2. Who will be the link trustee? The link trustee (probably you) will be the single person ultimately responsible for proper operation of the link. Unless it's directly connected to a repeater, the link will transmit under the trustee's call sign, typically from his own station. Usually, the link trustee is also the owner of the linking equipment, including the Internet connection.

3. Who will be the control operator(s)? Even if you have determined that continuous monitoring of the link is not required by the Rules, every station (in the US, anyway) must have at least one control operator. In effect, the control operator is a person delegated by the trustee to keep the link in proper operation. Control ops should be hams who are thoroughly familiar with the system, and have some means for controlling it remotely, particularly if it needs to be shut down for some special reason.

4. Who should be allowed to send commands to the link? Most linking systems have the option for stations on the link frequency to send DTMF signals to connect and disconnect the link. These codes are standard by default, but can also be customized in order to limit access to a specific group of users who know them. Should control of the link be limited to members of the club, for example, or be open to any ham who is passing through the area?

5. Should there be any access rules? By default, the link can connect to any other station on the network, at any time. But, for a variety of reasons, you may want to block connections to or from specific stations. For example, you might want to prevent connections to another repeater across town, since linking two machines with similar coverage areas might be counterproductive. Or, you might want to inhibit connections to conference servers or reflectors, if the repeater is already particularly busy. However, avoid the temptation to limit access to the link so that only a closed group of stations can use it. This runs counter to the philosophy of both *IRLP* and *EchoLink*, which are offered to the Amateur Radio Service on the principle of open access.

Some of these questions are hard to answer before the link is actually up and running, since you don't always know what to expect. One way to come up with a good operating policy is to start with the "defaults", and then revisit these questions after the link has been running for a couple of weeks.

ORGANIZING THE SPACE

Next, think about where and how the linking equipment will be set up. The spot needs ample space for the computer and its keyboard and monitor, access to both the Internet connection and the RF gear, and a good source of power. Personal computers should always use a surge-protected power outlet, and an uninterruptible power supply (UPS) is recommended.

Keep in mind that the link's computer can run in a completely "lights-out" environment. This means that there is no reason why the PC can't be placed in a locked, dark room, with no monitor connected to the PC. That's because all of the necessary functions, including software upgrades, can be performed through a remote terminal connected to the Internet. As long as you have the appropriate terminal software installed on your main home PC, you can always "call in" to your node's computer and do virtually any software-based tasks you need to do. However, a locally connected monitor is recommended for the initial set-up, and your PC's BIOS might insist on having a keyboard connected to the PC, even if it's never used.

RF GEAR

Then, consider what you might use as RF hardware. Unless the link will be co-located with a repeater, you will need a suitable FM transceiver (or transmitter-receiver pair) for the link. Some node owners insist on using commercial-grade equipment, but a dependable amateur-grade transceiver can work quite well, particularly if it is operated at less than its full rated power. In either case, both the power supply and the cooling arrangements should be selected with long, continuous key-down periods in mind. Built-in CTCSS encode and decode is recommended, particularly for use with repeaters (more on that later), and the rig must have some sort of COS or BUSY output to indicate that the squelch is open. Many modern VHF or UHF rigs that are "packet-ready" have a rear-panel connector with a COS signal, along with line-level audio inputs and outputs; these are ideal for use with Internet links. If you're chosen rig doesn't already have a COS pin, you might be able to modify it so that it does.

LINK ANTENNAS

Antenna systems for Internet links are generally simpler than those for repeaters, because Internet links aren't full duplex—there is no need to be transmitting and receiving at the same time. Thus, there's usually no need for a duplexer on a link antenna. As with repeaters and other FM stations, vertical polarization is the norm. If the link will be serving a local repeater, consider using a directional array, and operating with minimal power; for a simplex link, an omnidirectional antenna with gain is usually desirable.

REMOTE CONTROL

Even if your country's amateur regulations don't specifically require it, a radio or wireline control link is a good idea. If you (or your control operator) are always at an Internet terminal when the link is operating, you might not need anything more than the existing Internet-based wireline control link—you can log in to the link remotely to disconnect it, shut it down, or re-enable it. If not, an RF control receiver should be installed at the link site, tuned to a quiet frequency on a different band from the link transmitter itself. (In the US, an RF control link must be above 222.15 MHz.)

INTERNET CONNECTION

The computer you use for your Internet link must (of course) have some way of accessing the Internet. Not long ago, the only choices available to home users were dial-up accounts and expensive leased lines. Nowadays, in many parts of the world, "broadband" options are offered, and in many places, there is a choice among more than one.

Dial-Up Connections

Generally speaking, dial-up Internet service, using a conventional telephone line and modem, is the least attractive option. Dial-up connections usually are the slowest and least reliable of the bunch. If you have a clean telephone line and a good-quality, so-called "56k" V.90 modem, the top speed you can achieve is 53,000 bits per second (bps) downstream (*from* the Internet), and 33,600 bps upstream (*to* the Internet). In the US, the FCC limits the downstream speed to 53,000, and the protocol itself limits the upstream speed to 33,600. For peer-to-peer communication, such as VoIP, this means the very best dial-up data rate is 33,600 bps, since data is traveling in both directions.

But be careful! Your modem's connection speed, as reported by the computer when it dials in, can be misleading. Typically, it's reporting the *downstream* connection rate, which can be quite different than the *upstream* connection rate. Again, the actual throughput for VoIP is the lesser of these two figures. What's more, the effective rate can be diminished by noise or other interference on the line, and can even change in the middle of a connection.

This is not to say that there aren't many satisfied Internet linking enthusiasts who use dial-up lines. *EchoLink* fits itself easily into a 33,600 connection, and *IRLP*'s GSM codec works well over dial-up lines as well. But in many cases, the upstream speed is less than this ideal figure. What's more, dial-up connections tend to have the greatest variations in *latency* (delay from one end to the other), which can be very disruptive to smooth VoIP operation. Another problem is that noise on the line can cause the connection to the ISP to be dropped abruptly from time to time.

Cable Modem Service

One of the newer "broadband" offerings comes from the local cable TV provider. Many companies now offer Internet service through the cable system, using a *cable modem* installed in each household. This piggybacks two-way digital traffic on special RF channels, putting you and your neighbors on a kind of local-area network. In general, cable modem Internet service is an excellent choice for VoIP. Upstream speeds are usually 128 kbps or better, and downstream speeds are almost always at least 1.5 Mbps. The main disadvantage is that the service can slow down if many of your neighbors are using it at the same time, since the last-mile bandwidth is being shared among many subscribers. It also requires, of course, that you be a customer of your cable TV company, and thus might not be cost-effective if you receive TV service some other way.

Digital Subscriber Line (DSL)

Digital signals can travel a short distance over twisted-pair telephone lines, and many telephone companies (and others) now offer DSL service. This is a form of high-speed Internet service that rides over the existing telephone wiring to the phone company's switching center. In fact, it is usually possible to get DSL service without having to install a second telephone line, since analog and digital signals can co-exist on the same pair. A special DSL modem is required. DSL is also an excellent choice for VoIP. Although its top speeds are generally less than comparable cable-modem service, the bandwidth is fixed, since it isn't being shared with neighbors, so its actual speed may be higher than cable at many times of the day.

Satellite Service

Several companies now offer Internet service as an add-on to satellite-provided television service. For many consumers, this is a third option for broadband service, and for some, the *only* such option. Satellite-delivered Internet service can work for VoIP, but check first to be sure that the ISP will provide you with a true Internet address when you connect, rather than a translated address (see the next section for details). Sometimes, this is available as an extra-cost option.

One potential problem with satellite Internet service is the high latency introduced by the long path between your ground-based dish and the geostationary satellite it uses. However, this is not likely to be a problem for VoIP systems such as *IRLP* and *EchoLink* that use UDP protocols, since these protocols use no end-to-end acknowledgement of packets.

FIREWALLS, ROUTERS AND SECURITY SOFTWARE

In the early days of the Internet, computers could usually exchange information freely, simply by knowing each other's host name (or Internet address). Of the billions of possible Internet addresses, only a handful were in use, and virtually all of them were permanently assigned to specific computers.

Since that time, there have been two significant developments that have made the landscape more complex.

The first has been the increased focus on security. With so many millions of computers now directly connected to each other worldwide, there is clearly a need to keep the "bad guys" from breaking into computers remotely, or sending damaging forms of data.

The second has been the rise of shared IP addresses. As more homes and small businesses get broadband access (DSL or cable) as a replacement for dial-up, there has been a steady increase in the number of home/office computer networks, which (among other things) allow every computer in the home or office to share a single Internet connection. At the heart of these networks sits a special type of *router* that works as an Internet traffic cop, automatically translating the home's single Internet address to the correct "local" address of the PC being used.

Although these changes have brought benefits in convenience and security, they've made life more difficult for peer-to-peer applications, such as VoIP programs. These programs typically use pre-assigned *ports* to carry on their Internet conversations, and expect a direct path from one computer to another, rather than channeling everything through a central server. For example, *EchoLink* relies on UDP ports 5198 and 5199 being available at both ends of the path. This means that Internet users who want to use VoIP applications (such as Internet voice links) often must make changes to the configuration of their home-network equipment or their security software to let the VoIP traffic pass through.

Microsoft *Windows* applications are among the favorite targets of evildoers who create viruses and worms, and thus Internet security software has become a necessity on computers running *Windows*. Many of these programs, such as *ZoneAlarm* and *Norton Internet Security*, will prevent VoIP programs from working correctly, unless they've been specially configured. This is because VoIP software usually must be able to receive "unsolicited" data from a distant computer on the Internet, something that these products will block by default. The most secure work-around is to set up the security software so that it will allow the VoIP program to accept data on certain ports, rather than disabling the security software altogether.

Home networks can pose a problem if two or more computers, through a router, are sharing a single Internet address. Partners on the Internet can only "see" and send data to this one public address. So, when unsolicited data arrives from the Internet, how does the router know which computer in the household to send it to? It doesn't—unless you've configured it to *forward* certain packets of data to a specific machine. VoIP systems generally use a limited range of UDP ports, and most home network routers can be configured to forward a certain range of incoming ports to a certain PC.

Unfortunately, if there are hundred different makes and models of routers on the market today, there are a hundred different sets of instructions for setting them up. Most routers have a set of Web-based setup screens, but they all seem to use different commands, and even different terminology, for the various configuration options. Look for options such as "forwarding" or "server setup" in the router manufacturer's documentation. Then, check the firewall requirements in the documentation for the linking system you're setting up, and see if you can put two and two together.

One word of caution about setting up a home-network router: In a typical set-up, the router assigns a local address to each of your home PCs using a mechanism called *DHCP* (dynamic host configuration protocol). This works fine for most applications, but can sometimes cause headaches for VoIP operation. Why? If you're running DHCP, the IP address of your node's PC can change from time to time, and so you might have to update the forwarding configuration each time it changes. DHCP has the idea of "lease" on each address, which is periodically renewed, but some PC's release their address when they're restarted. As an alternative, check your router's documentation to see what range of addresses can be used for *static* addressing, then set up each of your PCs to use a different static address in that range.

LINKING INTERFACES

In the world of Internet linking, the device that sits between the PC and the RF gear is commonly called an *interface*, or a *linking interface*. In general terms, the interface performs the following tasks:

• Routes audio from the link receiver to the input of the computer's sound card;

• Routes audio from the output of the computer's sound card to the link transmitter;

- Allows software on the computer to key and un-key the link transmitter;
- Allows software on the computer to detect the presence of a incoming signal at the link receiver; and
- Allows software on the computer to detect DTMF digits captured by the link receiver.

The first three items are familiar to anyone who has dallied in the HF digital modes, or otherwise used sound-card software designed for Amateur Radio. As described in the next chapter, the sound card is the critical "gateway" between the analog and digital worlds. The sound card does most of the heavy lifting, so the remaining interface between the PC and the rig can be quite simple.

However, effective Internet linking also requires that the computer begin "transmitting" to the Internet when the squelch of the link receiver opens up. So, the fourth item above is needed, too. This can either be done by interfacing the COS signal from the receiver to a pin on the computer's serial or parallel port, or detecting the signal entirely in software, where the program monitors and reacts to the peak audio level from the receiver (similar to a VOX).

And since most Internet links can accept DTMF commands from mobile and portable users, some sort of DTMF decoder is required. Again, this can either be done in hardware or software. Hardware solutions usually use an inexpensive, high-performance DTMF decoder chip that connects to the PC's serial or parallel port. Application software can accomplish much the same thing by applying digital signal processing (DSP) functions to the receiver audio captured by the sound card.

The specific requirements for linking interfaces, and the options available, depend on the particular linking system you're planning to deploy. The sections that follow include more information about linking interfaces for *IRLP* and *EchoLink*.

SETTING UP AN IRLP NODE

To set up an *IRLP* node, you'll need the following items:
- Link transceiver with COS output signal.
- Intel Pentium-based computer, with at least 32 MB of memory. The computer must have a Sound Blaster sound card and a parallel port.
- Internet connection for the computer. A full-time "broadband" connection, such as a DSL or cable-modem service, is strongly recommended.
- *IRLP* interface board (see **Figure 5.1**). A diagram of a typical IRLP node is shown in **Figure 5.2**.

Figure 5.1—A close-up of the *IRLP* 3.0 interface board. The DB-25 connector on the right connects to the PC's parallel port. The four-pin connector at the top accepts the 12VDC power, and the 10-pin header at the top left goes to a DB-9 connector to which the link transceiver and the sound card connect. The board comes with brackets for mounting the board and the DB-9 connector inside the computer, or it can be housed in an external enclosure. (*Paul Cassel, VE3SY*)

Figure 5.2—Diagram of a typical *IRLP* node. (*Paul Cassel, VE3SY*)

- Custom-made cable(s) to connect *IRLP* interface board to transceiver and sound card. "Plug and play" cables for a few popular radios are also available.
- *IRLP* software.
- *Linux* operating system software.

IRLP makes the process easier by offering a package that includes the *IRLP* interface board and a CD-ROM with both the *IRLP* software and a copy of Red Hat *Linux* (**Figure 5.3**). This is the recommended way to get started.

COS Output Signal

The *IRLP* software needs to be able to sense the presence of an incoming signal from the transceiver. Basically, it needs to know the state of the receiver's squelch circuit—when the squelch is open, a signal is assumed to be present, and when it's closed, no signal is assumed.

This means that the transceiver you plan to use for your *IRLP* node will need to provide a dc voltage that goes from low to high (or vice versa) when the squelch opens. This signal is sometimes called COS, for *carrier-operated squelch* or *carrier-operated switch*. A pin on the interface board's DB-9 connector accepts this signal and passes it along to the software.

With many modern transceivers, getting a COS signal is dead simple—a back-panel mini-DIN connector provides audio input and output, push-to-talk, and COS (sometimes called "busy"), all in one place. That's partly be-

Figure 5.3—The complete *IRLP* package includes all required software (including *Linux*), the interface board and cables to connect the board to the PC. (*Paul Cassel, VE3SY*)

cause these signals are commonly used to connect a terminal node controller (TNC) to the transceiver for packet operation. All that's needed is a single cable with a properly wired mini-DIN or DB-9 connector to make all the connections between the rig and the computer.

With other equipment, finding a suitable COS signal is more of challenge. However, with the help of a schematic, you can probably find what you're looking for, and figure out a way to wire it to the interface board. The board can be jumpered several ways to accommodate the voltage and sense of the available COS signal.

Installation Steps

1. Download an *IRLP* order form from the main *IRLP* Web site (**www.irlp.net**), and send it to the address provided.

2. Gather and prepare the necessary computer and RF equipment, including the Internet connection.

3. When the *IRLP* kit arrives, an instruction sheet will direct you to the last versions of the installation documents, which you can download from a special Web site. These instructions include:

- Information on how to install the *IRLP* interface board. This is normally installed inside the computer itself, as long as there's room for it (**Figure 5.4**).

- Detailed steps for installing *Linux*, using the installation CD provided in the kit.

- Detailed steps for installing the *IRLP* software, also from the installation CD.

- Information on how to generate the necessary public and private keys for PGP, and how to submit the public key to the *IRLP* system.

- Instructions for how to test the node, and adjust audio levels.

4. Install the interface board.

5. Create the necessary audio and control cables to connect the PC to your link equipment.

6. Install *Linux* and the *IRLP* software.

7. Configure the software.

8. Test the system, and adjust audio levels.

9. Submit the details of your new node to the *IRLP* Web site.

Once you are registered as an *IRLP* node owner, you'll be welcomed to join the *IRLP* Owner's forum on Yahoo (**www.yahoogroups.com**). The archives of this Yahoo group are an excellent repository of information on node setup, adjustment and troubleshooting. You'll also be able to download the *Unofficial IRLP Manual and Troubleshooting Guide*, a compendium of advice assembled from various sources (including the Yahoo group) by Jim Price, WW4M.

Figure 5.4—The *IRLP* interface board installed inside an HP Vectra PC at K1RFD.

Getting Friendly with *Linux*

One of the first pieces of advice for new *IRLP* node owners is to become familiar with the *Linux* operating system. *Linux* will seem natural to anyone who has used Unix, but might seem foreign at first to those who are accustomed to Microsoft *Windows*, or versions of the Macintosh operating system prior to OS X. There are several excellent books on *Linux* that are geared specifically to new users.

Although not officially a "flavor" of *UNIX*, *Linux* is a very *UNIX*-like operating system. It was designed from the ground up to run on commodity computers based on the Intel chipset, which means it runs very efficiently, even on the most modest of hardware. It also provides considerable flexibility in how it is installed. The version of *Linux* shipped in the *IRLP* kit is a streamlined version of the Red Hat distribution. Since it is essentially a "server" application (as opposed to a "workstation" application), *IRLP* has no need for a graphical user interface (GUI), so no GUI is installed in a normal set-up. This means that virtually all of the installation, set-up, and day-to-day control of the system is done with a command-line interface, rather than mouse clicks on a virtual desktop.

Although this may sound rather Spartan to those accustomed to using a mouse, it has two important benefits. The first is that it makes best use of the system resources. A GUI requires a lot of memory and processing power, so why install a GUI when it's not needed? The second is that it makes it easy to install *IRLP* in a completely lights-out environment. Although a keyboard and monitor are required for the initial setup, they can easily be disconnected afterward, and the computer moved to a closet or under a desk somewhere. As long as the computer has a reliable power supply and Internet connection, it is always accessible (and completely controllable) from a remote terminal running a console program such as *ssh*.

Up and Running with IRLP

The steps for installing the *IRLP* hardware and software are well documented, but do change from time to time. When you receive the *IRLP* kit, you'll be directed to a Web site with complete step-by-step instructions on how to proceed.

For most installations, the only "hardware" steps are installing the *IRLP* board (usually inside the PC), and creating a cable to connect the link transceiver to the board. This cable carries the audio input and output signals, as well as the COS signal from the receiver and the PTT signal to the transmitter. Command-line utilities are included in the *IRLP* software package for testing the connection once it's completed. For example, the rig can be keyed and un-keyed by typing special commands, and the status of the COS and DTMF decoders can be monitored.

Figure 5.4 shows a typical *IRLP* interface board installation, as it appears inside the computer. The board itself occupies a back-panel slot (although not a motherboard slot), on which the DB-25 connector is mounted. A cable from the DB-25 connector plugs into the computer's parallel port. A ribbon cable connects the board to a DB-9 connector, which can be mounted in another back-panel slot on the PC.

Scripts drive most of the *IRLP* software installation and configuration steps. This will be familiar territory to anyone who has installed *Linux* or Unix software packages. The scripts create all necessary directories, copy files, and set permissions.

One of the steps you'll be asked to do is to create a *key pair*. This is a "public" key and a "private" key that are used in the PGP-based authentication process each time a connection is established. A particularly important step is to copy your key pair to a backup diskette, so that you can recover from a system failure, if necessary, by re-installing the software. Without a backup of your private key, you'd have to create a new key pair and register it with the *IRLP* system before getting back online.

Typically, there are only two adjustments that will need to be made to the software. The first is to set the audio levels on the sound card. The easiest way to do this is with a utility called *aumix* (**Figure 5.5**), which displays a set of virtual mixer controls as sliders. The installation guide describes a procedure in which you ask the *IRLP* software to generate a test tone through the sound card, and then use aumix to adjust the audio level into your link transmitter while you monitor the output with a receiver.

The second adjustment is the "pulseback delay." This is a feature that prevents the software from reacting to a false COS signal whenever your link transmitter goes key-up. On a repeater link, this can be caused by the link transceiver hearing its own squelch tail; on a simplex link, it can be a COS pulse coming from the transceiver itself. With the link transceiver set up and tuned to the chosen frequency, there's a utility that will key the rig briefly, detect, and adjust the correct pulseback delay time automatically.

Customization

IRLP offers many opportunities for customization, since the software is organized around a set of building-block components that are driven by scripts. For example, you can write or modify scripts to turn the link on and off at certain times, or respond to special DTMF sequences with control functions. Several useful examples of custom scripts are posted in the Files area of the Yahoo group for *IRLP* node owners. *IRLP* scripts are also discussed in more detail in Chapter 8.

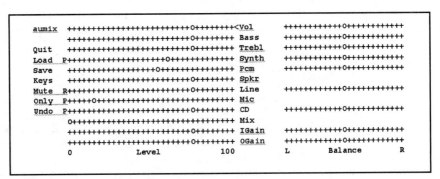

Figure 5.5—The *aumix* utility for *Linux*.

One thing you'll almost certainly need to customize is the station ID. *IRLP* doesn't have a built-in provision for sending a Morse or voice ID over the link, so unless your *IRLP* gear is directly connected to a repeater, you'll need to set up some way for it to identify itself periodically while the link is in use.

A neat "trick" for generating a Morse ID without interfering with the normal function of the node is to use the sound card's on-board music synthesizer to generate a tone. The sound card's mixer will combine the Morse tone from the synthesizer with the sampled audio path, so the two are heard simultaneously over the link. To make this work, you can download and compile a simple *C*-language program (called *sccw*, for "sound card CW") that sends a string of Morse characters through the synthesizer with proper timing. Another downloadable script polls the state of the system to determine when the ID should be aired, and then calls *sccw* with your node's call sign at the appropriate times to generate the ID. With the right adjustments to the script, the exact timing and triggering of the ID can be set up any way you wish.

SETTING UP AN ECHOLINK NODE

To set up an *EchoLink* RF node, you'll need the following items:
- Link transceiver.
- Intel Pentium-based computer, with sufficient memory to meet the minimum requirements for the version of *Windows* you are running. The computer must have a sound card (or built-in sound device) and a serial port. If the computer has a USB port but no serial port, a USB-to-serial adapter can be used.
- Internet connection for the computer. A "broadband" connection, such as a DSL or cable-modem service, is recommended, although a dial-up connection can also be used.
- Suitable interface device. A number of different devices can be used, including PC-to-rig interfaces designed for HF digital modes.
- Cable(s) to connect the PC and the interface to the transceiver. The interface manufacturer may have already provided these cables.
- Microsoft *Windows* (*Windows 95* or above).
- *EchoLink* software.

You can buy any of the commonly available PC-to-rig interfaces, or purchase a "linking" interface that has been specifically designed for use with *EchoLink*. Or, you can build a simple interface circuit yourself.

If you're inclined to build an interface circuit yourself, you may be surprised to learn that the most basic homebrew interface is extremely simple (**Figure 5.6**). You might even be able to stuff it inside the shell of a DB-9 connector.

Figure 5.6—A basic homebrew computer-to-rig interface for *EchoLink*.

Figure 5.7—RIGblaster models offered by West Mountain Radio. These interfaces can also be used with HF digital mode software. (*West Mountain Radio*)

In this circuit, the transceiver's audio output goes directly to the line input of the PC's sound card. The speaker output of the sound card goes to the microphone input of the transceiver, through a 20 dB attenuator. For transmit control, the RTS pin of the COM port engages the rig's PTT control by turning on an NPN transistor. That's all there is to it! To set up *EchoLink* to use this simple interface, use the settings shown in **Figures 5.9 and 5.10**.

This circuit is very bare bones, of course, and assumes that you can get away with having a single, common ground between the two devices, without hum or feedback due to ground loops. One of the advantages of using a more complex, ready-to-run interface board is that most of these problems are avoided, since inputs and outputs often have dc isolation.

Examples of PC-to-rig interfaces are the RIGblaster models offered by West Mountain Radio (**Figure 5.7**), the Soundcard Radio Interface from MFJ Enterprises, the Tigertronics SignaLink and the BuxComm Rascal. Note that these are soundcard-to-radio interfaces, not TNCs, designed primarily for HF digital modes such as PSK31. They all connect to the serial port and

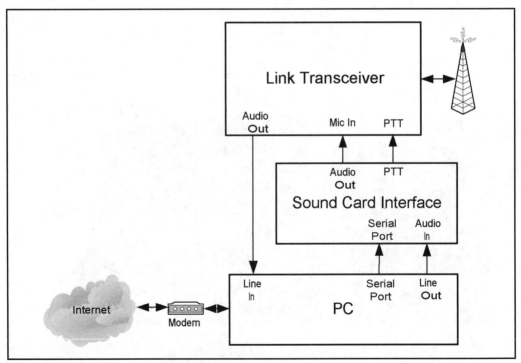

Figure 5.8—Block diagram of the connections with a general-purpose sound card interface, such as the RIGblaster *nomic*. This type of interface handles only the PTT and audio connections to the transmitter; the receiver audio goes directly to the PC's sound card.

Figure 5.9—The RX Control tab of *EchoLink*'s Sysop Setup, showing typical settings for VOX control.

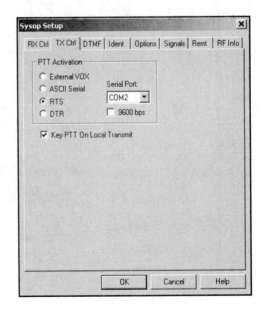

Figure 5.10—The TX Control tab of *EchoLink*'s Sysop Setup, showing typical settings for use with a generic sound card interface, such as the type used for HF digital modes.

Figure 5.11—WB2REM and G4CDY's AMI board in its optional enclosure. (*James Millner, WB2REM*)

Figure 5.12—WB2REM and G4CDY's Ultimate Linking Interface, or ULI. (*WB2REM*)

sound card of the PC, and to the microphone input of the transceiver, and provide a way for the computer software to key the rig's PTT line via the serial port (**Figure 5.8**). When using one of these generic interfaces, DTMF commands are detected by *EchoLink*'s software-based DTMF decoder, and VOX is used for carrier detect.

Linking interfaces, on the other hand, have been designed specifically for VoIP software such as *EchoLink*. In addition to keying the transceiver on command, these devices have on-board DTMF decoders, and provisions for connecting a second receiver as a control link. Some have extra features such as auxiliary device outputs that can be switched on and off with DTMF commands, and extra connectors for routing audio inputs and outputs. Some can also be used with HF digital mode software, such as PSK31 or RTTY programs. Several models of linking interfaces are available from WB2REM (**Figures 5.11, 5.12 and 5.13**), VA3TO (**Figure 5.14**) and G3VFP. The original WB2REM board was described in *QST* for March, 2002. **Figures 5.15 and 5.16** show the general hookups between these linking interfaces and the PC and link transceiver. An example of a more complex hook-up, featuring both a link transceiver and a control-link receiver, is shown in **Figure 5.17**. This example uses the VA3TO interface, but a similar arrangement can be used with some of the other types.

Figure 5.13—The ULI board in its optional enclosure. (*K1RFD*)

Figure 5.14—The VA3TO board in its optional enclosure, with the cover removed. The matrix of solder pads on the left-hand side is a prototyping area where additional components can be added. (*K1RFD*)

DIRECT REPEATER CONNECTIONS

If your node will serve a local repeater, you may have the option of operating the link through a transceiver tuned to the frequency pair of the repeater, or wiring the link directly to the repeater at the repeater site. There are pros and cons to each approach.

The main advantage of a remote link (i.e., through a transceiver located some distance from the repeater) is accessibility. The computer and linking equipment can be in any convenient location in earshot of the repeater, making it easier to maintain and monitor. It also might be the only option if no Internet connection is available at the repeater site.

However, some clubs have decided to set up the node at the repeater site, and connect it directly to the repeater equipment. The main advantage is smoother integration—the node's input can receive a signal directly from the repeater receiver, and there's no need for the node to generate its own ID, since it doesn't transmit its own signal. The link can piggyback on the repeater's emergency power supply, in scenarios where the power goes out but Internet connectivity remains. Also, in some situations, there are legal issues that make it impractical to operate the node as a separate station.

Connections between the node controller and the repeater equipment are usually straightforward. **Figure 5.18** is a block diagram of typical connec-

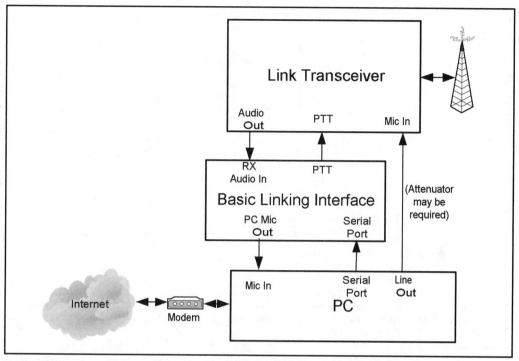

Figure 5.15—Block diagram of the connections with a basic special-purpose linking interface, such as the WB2REM Rev B board. Receiver audio is routed through the interface, rather than going directly to the PC's sound card, because the interface has a built-in DTMF decoder.

tions between a linking interface and a simple repeater system. The node is wired so that it takes its COS signal and audio directly from the receiver. On the transmit side, the PTT signal is logically ORed with the receiver's COS signal, but audio is routed directly to the transmitter, to prevent any DTMF signals received over the link from triggering control functions of the repeater itself.

Some repeater controllers come with "remote base" connections built in. This simplifies the wiring, since all connections are made between the linking interface and the repeater controller. It also may allow the node to be enabled and disabled directly through the repeater controller using DTMF commands, either over the air or through the repeater's existing control link.

Clearly, it's important to choose reliable equipment if the node is to be placed at the repeater site. Just as you would select commercial-grade RF gear for your repeater, you should choose a business-class (or server-class) personal computer with conservatively rated components. Computers generate a great deal of heat, and the more rugged models tend to have higher fan capacities and larger power supplies. High performance computers are

Figure 5.16—Block diagram of the connections with an advanced special-purpose linking interface. With this device, audio in both directions is routed through the linking interface. The carrier-detect connection is optional.

Figure 5.17—A complete hook-up diagram of an advanced node set-up using the VA3TO linking interface. The system has a control receiver in addition to the main link transceiver. (*Hugh Duff, VA3TO*)

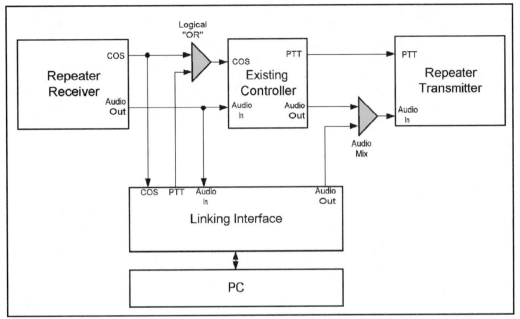

Figure 5.18—A block diagram of typical connections between a node's linking interface and the repeater equipment.

not required for Internet linking, so you might find a local business that is willing to donate an older machine that's several years out of date but still very reliable. For this purpose, an older 200 MHz machine with redundant power supplies and mirrored drives is clearly superior to a "top of the line" 3 GHz machine built for the consumer market.

Reliability applies to software, too. *Linux* has an excellent track record for reliability and stability, so you'll be in fine shape if you are setting up an *IRLP* node. If you plan to run a *Windows*-based node, the best choice for *Windows* is a version based on the NT kernel, such as *Windows 2000, Windows XP,* or *Windows Server 2003*. These systems also have excellent uptimes when properly configured.

Reliable remote control of the PC is important when the computer is remotely located. Internet access is already taken care of, so the only remaining piece is software that will provide complete and secure control of the machine from a distant location. For *Windows* systems, *Windows* Terminal Services is available for server-class versions of the OS, and *Windows XP Professional* offers Remote Desktop as an option. You can also use a product such as *ControlIT, pcAnywhere* or *WinVNC*. For *Linux* systems running *IRLP*, remote command-line access is available through *ssh* (secure shell). *ssh* clients (such as *PuTTY*, from **www.chiark.greenend.org.uk/~sgtatham/putty**) are available for several popular platforms.

Chapter 6

Digital Audio and the Internet

The computer's sound card is one of its most versatile input-output (I/O) devices, particularly for Amateur Radio communication. But it's also one of the least well understood. In this section, we'll go on a tour of the innards of the typical PC sound device, and explore how it's used for digital voice modes such as VoIP.

First, I should point out that many modern PC's have audio capability built in to the computer, directly on the motherboard. Others have a sound card plugged into an expansion slot, such as a PCI slot, instead. To keep the language simple, I'll refer to both types of sound hardware as "sound cards."

ANALOG TO DIGITAL, AND BACK AGAIN

Sound is reproduced electrically by using devices such as microphones and speakers, which convert audio-frequency variations in air pressure into varying electrical signals (**Figure 6.1**). A device called an analog-to-digital converter (A/D) produces a binary number proportional to an input voltage, and a digital-to-analog converter (D/A) does just the reverse. At its heart, the computer's sound card is simply an analog-to-digital converter that works at audio frequencies. In fact, it's both an A/D and D/A converter, since it can detect analog signals as well as create them. Just like any other analog-to-digital converter, the sound card converts an incoming voltage into a binary number, and vice versa. But since it's designed to capture and reproduce sound, it *samples* the incoming signal (takes a measurement of it) at a precise, periodic rate—an audio rate (**Figure 6.2**). So rather than converting a dc voltage into a single binary number, the sound card is measuring the volt-

Figure 6.1—A typical audio waveform.

age thousands of times per second, converting each measurement (or sample) into a number, and storing each of the numbers in sequence into a block of the computer's memory, called a *buffer*. Going the other direction, the sound card can take the contents of a buffer and convert each sample into a corresponding voltage at the same precise rate.

What makes this extremely useful is that the sound card is converting an audio-frequency waveform to and from its digital equivalent. The more precise the measurement, and the faster the sample rate, the more accurate this conversion becomes. A principle known as the *Nyquist theorem* tells us that the highest frequency we can accurately capture is one-half the frequency at which we are sampling. So a sound card that is sampling at 44,100 samples per second can capture audio frequencies up to 22,050 cycles per second, or about 22 kHz—roughly the highest frequency most people can hear. (Dogs may wish to use a higher sample rate.)

Besides sample rate, the other important consideration is the precision (resolution) of the sound card's analog-to-digital conversion. Each voltage sample is converted into a binary number, and every binary number is a collection of bits (binary digits). Just as with decimal digits, the more binary digits in the sample, the wider the range of values that can be represented. A/D converters are said to have a certain number of *bits of resolution,* and thus, so are sound cards. Most sound cards can sample at either 8 bits or 16 bits.

The more bits of resolution, the greater the *dynamic range*—the difference in amplitude between the strongest signal the sound card can measure,

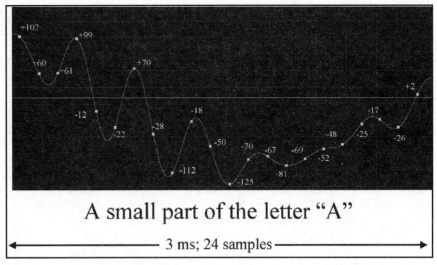

Figure 6.2—Digital sampling of an audio signal.

and the weakest—and, similarly, the greater the maximum signal-to-noise ratio. With 8-bit sampling, there are 2^8, or 256, different voltage levels the sound card can measure. This works out to a maximum dynamic range of about 48 dB. With 16-bit sampling, the number of different voltage levels jumps to 65536, for 96 dB. (Recall that since we're dealing with voltage, rather than power, dynamic range in dB = 20 $\log_{10}$ R, where R is the ratio of strongest signal to weakest signal.)

As with any electronic system, noise comes into the picture, and some sound cards are noisier than others. With no signal present on the input, you might find that the sound card is not producing a pure zero level. Since the true dynamic range is the difference between the strongest signal and the noise floor, the actual dynamic range of a given sound card might be somewhat less than the theoretical figures above.

Putting all of this together, we realize that faithfully capturing and stor-

Table 6.1

Common Sample Rates

Sample Rate	Bandwidth	Typical Application
44 kHz	22 kHz	CD-quality music
22 kHz	11 kHz	Radio-quality music
11 kHz	5.5 kHz	Radio-quality voice
8 kHz	4 kHz	Two-way voice communications

ing an audio signal as digital data means using a high sample rate and lots of bits of resolution. Again with apologies to the dogs that might be reading this, we humans can hear up to about 22,000 Hz. Our ears have about 100 dB of dynamic range, and we have two of them. So to faithfully reproduce the sound of a symphony orchestra, we'd want to set our sound cards to sample at 44 kHz, 16 bits per sample, and in two channels at the same time (left and right, for stereo). As it turns out, this is exactly how an audio compact disc (CD) is recorded.

The bad news is that it requires lots of data storage. A 16-bit stereo recording requires 4 bytes of storage per sample. At 44,100 samples per second, that's 176,400 bytes for each *second* of high-fidelity sound.

Despite the noble efforts of hams experimenting with hi-fi SSB, the fact is that most radio communications systems are not hi-fi, by design. Usually, the important thing is to get the message through—and this means that *intelligibility* is paramount. Studies have shown that the frequencies 300 to 3000 Hz are where most of the action is, in terms of understanding what the other person is saying. Not only that, but the audio dynamic range of most communications systems is a lot less than 96 dB. For these reasons, the makers of telephone equipment—the pioneers in VoIP technology—decided that an 8 kHz sample rate and 8-bit resolution were most appropriate for communications systems. This provides about 4000 Hz of bandwidth, about 48 dB of dynamic range, and requires 8000 bytes of storage for each second of audio.

There's a certain amount of psychology to audio quality. If you were to make an audio recording of your voice at 8 bits and 8000 Hz, and then play it back (using a program such as *Windows* Sound Recorder) through your computer speakers, you'd probably think that it sounded terribly "narrow" and tinny, especially compared to one of the higher sample rates. But try the same experiment listening to the results over a 2-meter simplex frequency. You'll probably discover that the sound coming from your handheld transceiver is just fine, and that it sounds more like a live transmission than a recording. And most importantly, you'll probably understand every single word quite clearly.

COMPRESSION

A stream of digital audio sampled at 8 bits, 8000 Hz requires 8000 bytes of storage per second. This means it can be transmitted from one computer to another at a minimum rate of 8000 bytes per second, or 64,000 bits per second, without needing extra time to "catch up". In this example, 64,000 bits per second, or roughly 64 kilobits per second, is the *data rate* of the digital signal from one computer to another. If the signal is moving over a single pair of wires, such as a telephone line or an Internet connection, you'd expect that the connection would need to have a *bandwidth* of 64 kHz.

Fortunately, mathematicians and computer scientists have figured out ways to do more with less. Bandwidth is expensive, so it would be cheaper and more practical to squeeze this same digital signal through a narrower "pipe." One of the most effective techniques for doing this is *compression*.

Compression is the art and science of squeezing a long stream of bits down to a shorter stream by taking out repetitive information. My wife never fails to remind me when I begin telling her the same story twice. When I begin to see her eyes roll, I know she's already heard it. So instead, I could give each of my jokes and stories a number, and just say "Honey, 4552!" This would save a lot of unnecessary bandwidth. (She still wouldn't laugh, but at least we'd avoid the rolling pupils.)

The same holds true for digital information. A computer can be programmed to look for repeating patterns in the signal, such as frequently used words, and substitute each with a much shorter digital abbreviation. The opposite task, *decompression*, involves putting the signal back the way it was by reversing this procedure. All of this takes a little more processing power at both ends, but can often save a lot of bandwidth. The difference in size between the original signal and the compressed signal is called the *compression ratio*.

Less Is More

There are two flavors of compression, for different purposes: *lossy* and *lossless*. With lossless compression, the decompressed signal is identical to the original—no information is lost. With lossy compression, the decompressed signal is a little different—something has become lost in the translation.

So why be lossy when you can be lossless? It depends on the kind of information being processed. If it's a financial spreadsheet, every digit and decimal point is important, so lossless is the only way to go. But if it's a representation of something we see or hear, we can easily afford to lose some information, if it's a detail we'd never notice. And the big benefit of lossy compression is that it can give us much better compression ratios.

If you've ever worked with a digital camera, you're probably heard of the JPEG file format. JPEG files use an ingenious type of lossy compression that's specially designed for photographic images. By removing certain details that the human eye doesn't notice, an enormous number of bytes can be saved.

The same idea applies to audio data. Special compression techniques can be applied to a digital audio signal to remove unimportant information, yielding a decompressed version that sounds almost the same as the original, and again saving lots of bytes in transit.

A computer program that compresses and decompresses data is called a *codec* (an abbreviation for compressor-decompressor). Frequently, audio codecs are designed to work with signals with a specific sample rate. For example, *EchoLink* uses the GSM (Global System for Mobile Communications) codec, which squeezes an 8-bit, 8000 Hz signal from 64,000 bits per second down to 13,200 bits per second. This makes it possible to send a GSM-compressed audio signal over a narrowband connection, such as a conventional telephone line with a dial-up modem at each end. Another example is ADPCM (adaptive differential pulse-code modulation), which works at any of several different sample rates, and provides less compression, but generally better audio quality. *EchoLink* uses GSM, and *IRLP* can use either ADPCM or GSM.

STREAMING AUDIO AND THE INTERNET

There's been plenty of talk recently about *streaming* audio and video over the Internet. Streaming audio is at the heart of a VoIP system. But exactly does it mean?

To explain, let's begin with some background on how information moves from one place to another over the Internet. An Internet connection can actually use any of several *protocols* to transfer data. The one most commonly used is TCP, or Transmission Control Protocol. When two computers are exchanging data using TCP, they are said to be *connected* over a TCP *session*.

The "connection" between the two computers, in this sense, is really just an abstraction. But it's a powerful concept. When a TCP session has been established, a program on one machine can send data to a program on the other machine, and be assured that the message will arrive exactly as it was sent, with no loss of information, no matter how big the message is, or what kind of data it contains. This assurance is known as *guaranteed delivery*. It's the same "guarantee" that an amateur packet network makes when two stations connect using AX.25. In essence, TCP allows the two machines to set up a temporary, virtual circuit, over which information can be reliably transferred.

Although TCP guarantees the delivery of the message (as long as the virtual circuit isn't interrupted), it makes no guarantees as to how long it will take to transmit it. Over a clean, fat pipe, it could take a fraction of a second. Over a thin, noisy circuit, it could take a lot longer, because so few of the packets arrive at their destination intact—TCP re-transmits them until all have been verified.

This is great for certain kinds of messages, like e-mail messages and (to some extent) Web pages. We're willing to a wait a couple of extra seconds for these messages to arrive at their destination intact. But it poses a dilemma for real-time data, such as audio, which has to arrive *promptly* at its destination, and with a predictable delay. If you speak the word "radio," imagine what would happen if the word was split into three packets—one for each syllable—and the "ray" and the "dee" made it across almost instantly, but the "oh" was delayed by a couple of seconds. It would introduce either a two-second gap between syllables, or a two-second delay for the whole word.

The problem lies in the fact that the Internet, at its basic protocol level, makes no guarantees about whether packets will arrive, or when, or even in what order. This presents a serious challenge for real-time audio and video applications, for which time is of the essence. These applications are sometimes called *isochronous*, since they must process regular amounts of data at fixed intervals. The best kind of network for streaming audio and video is one that has a fixed amount of *latency*, or delay, from one end to the other. Unfortunately, this isn't generally true of the Internet.

To meet the challenge, there's another commonly used Internet protocol, called User Datagram Protocol, or UDP. Unlike TCP, UDP is "unconnected"—there is no virtual circuit between peers, and no implicit guarantees about how packets will be delivered. The only guarantee is that errors can be detected, so the receiver can ignore any packets that arrive garbled. It's analogous to the AX.25 UI frames used by APRS.

How does this improve the landscape for real-time audio and video? Unlike TCP, UDP has no built-in handshaking or acknowledgement mechanism. Packets are sent from one computer to the other in fire-and-forget fashion. If a given packet doesn't arrive at its destination, neither the sender nor the receiver is any the wiser. This significantly reduces the overhead of acknowledgements and re-tries, and makes the latency more predictable. With UDP, the only thing getting in the way of seeing a nice, even stream of packets at the other end is the variability of the Internet itself.

But hold on a second—if UDP doesn't guarantee that each packet will get delivered, doesn't this mean that the receiver might miss some parts of the message? Absolutely. But this is an acceptable tradeoff for audio and video applications, which are normally intended for consumption by human eyes and ears. Just as lossy compression is an acceptable tradeoff for squeezing the size of an audio data stream, so is the non-guaranteed nature of UDP. When we stream data using UDP, we're saying, "It's better to miss a syllable here and there, than to wait a long time for the message to get through, just because a couple of syllables were missed."

The Jitter Bug

I hinted earlier that the latency of the Internet is unpredictable. If Computer A sends two UDP packets to Computer B over the Internet, the first one might take 50 milliseconds to arrive, and the second one might take 5000 milliseconds to arrive. The most common reason for the extra delay is simply network congestion; somewhere along the line, a buffer gets tempo-

Figure 6.3—Constant latency.

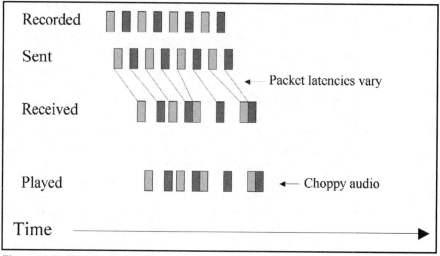

Figure 6.4—Variable latency.

rarily backlogged with packets to send.

Variations in latency are often called *jitter*. Compare **Figures 6.3** and **6.4**. For streaming audio to work smoothly, the system needs to have a way to compensate for jitter. This is usually done at the receiving end, since the fire-and-forget sender rarely knows how long packets are taking to arrive. And, it's usually done using a memory structure called a *buffer*.

Imagine a checkout line in a supermarket. I take the items out of the cart and put them on the conveyor belt; the cashier, working from the other end of the belt, scans them and tosses them in bags. Naturally, however, the cashier does his job a lot more smoothly than I do mine. While I struggle to lift the extra-large jug of Dreft from the bottom of the cart, and explain to my daughter why the jumbo Butterfinger on the candy rack would not be a wise purchase, the cashier is scanning item after item like clockwork. How is this possible?

The answer, of course, is the conveyor belt. It doesn't make anything go faster, but it sure does make things go more smoothly. Even though I'm putting items on the belt at various different rates, the cashier is scanning them at a smooth two items per second. As long as my average rate is at least two items per second, and there are always some items waiting in line on the belt, the cashier never has to wait for me. I have lots of jitter, but the cashier never notices it.

Computer software for receiving streaming audio usually has a digital "conveyor belt" built into it. This is certainly the case with Internet linking systems such as *EchoLink* and *IRLP*. This jitter compensation buffer is a queue, which fills up with incoming UDP packets at one end, and empties them into the sound card (or codec) from the other. The queue is large enough that it can compensate for most variations in latency, but small enough that it doesn't introduce too much extra delay (**Figure 6.5**). As you can see, this is a tradeoff, and it is usually adjustable.

Besides smoothing out jitter, there's another benefit to having this buffer. Recall that UDP makes no guarantee about whether packets will ever arrive,

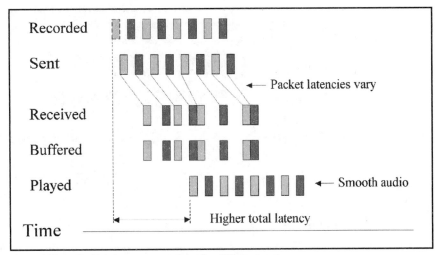

Figure 6.5—Buffer to compensate for jitter.

or in what order. In fact, it doesn't even guarantee that the receiver won't get duplicate packets. To help the receiver detect these problems, a program that sends streaming audio usually marks each successive packet with a serial number or a timestamp. Then, when packets arrive at the receiver, the receiver can try to ensure that they are placed in the buffer in the correct order. If packet 123 arrives just ahead of packet 122, the packets can be re-ordered in the buffer. Similarly, if two copies of packet 123 arrive, the receiver can detect it by seeing that it already has a copy of 123 in its buffer.

The receiver can also detect missing packets. If 122, 123, and 125 arrive, but 124 never does, it will be quite evident when the receiver pulls 123 from the buffer, sends it to the sound card, and then notices that next in line is 125. At this point, the receiver might want to insert a blank (or duplicate) packet to take the place of the AWOL 124, to ensure that the timing doesn't suffer.

Staying in Sync

Now that we've addressed the problem of jitter, there's another problem to contend with. It's the problem of synchronization.

The sending computer is sampling an audio signal at 8000 samples per second, compressing the data, and transmitting it over the Internet to the receiver. The receiver is accepting this data, decompressing it, and converting it back to an analog signal, also at 8000 samples per second. Everything is working well.

But what if the sender's sound card is actually running at 7920 samples

Figure 6.6—Timing mismatch: Sender running slower than receiver.

per second, instead of exactly 8000—one percent slower (**Figure 6.6**)? It means that the receiver's card is running slightly faster by comparison, and thus will eventually become starved for data—the sender won't be feeding it packets fast enough, and sooner or later, the digital conveyor belt will become empty. Unless we do something about it, we'll start hearing gaps in the audio.

It seems like a minor mismatch (only one percent), but if you work out the math, you'll see it can be a real problem. If we're sending 12.5 packets per second, each packet contains 640 samples. If the sender is running 80 samples per second slower than the receiver, it means the receiver will fall behind at the rate of one packet every 8 seconds. If the jitter buffer normally holds 500 ms worth of data (about 6 packets), the buffer will be completely empty after 48 seconds, well within the duration of a typical transmission.

The opposite situation can be a problem, too. If the sender is running faster than the receiver, the receiver's buffer will start to get bigger and bigger (**Figure 6.7**). Assuming there's plenty of memory, the total delay from sender to receiver will start to grow, making it extremely difficult to carry on a two-way conversation.

Although most sound cards are crystal-controlled, there seems to be a wide variation in their actual sample rates when they are asked to operate at the nominal rate of 8000 Hz. This may be due to the architecture of the individual cards, particularly the way the crystal frequency is divided down to produce the actual codec clock. Spot-check testing has shown that some cards are off by as much as two percent.

There are several ways to address this problem. The most obvious is to adjust the sample rate of the receiver's sound card so it's exactly in tune

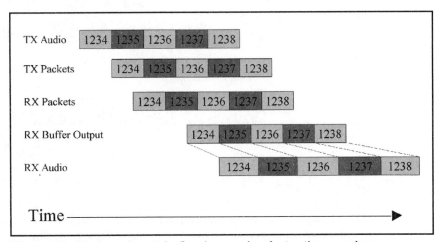

Figure 6.7—Timing mismatch: Sender running faster than receiver.

with the average rate at which packets are arriving from the sender. However, many sound cards do not allow this kind of fine-tuning, so it's not a universal solution. Another approach is to use DSP functions to convert the sender's sample rate to the receiver's sample rate; in effect, doing the fine-tuning in software. That may be computationally intensive, and might introduce unpleasant artifacts in the recovered audio.

A compromise solution is to make the adjustments by adding or removing entire packets. This is the approach used by *EchoLink* (**Figure 6.8**). The receiver's software keeps an eye on the average size of the jitter buffer. If the buffer seems to be consistently shrinking in size over time, it will insert an extra packet of silence to compensate for it. If, however, the buffer seems to be growing over time, it pulls a packet out of it. This technique is fully self-adjusting, since the act of adding or removing a packet immediately returns the buffer to its normal size, after which the process begins all over again.

How does this sound at the receiving end? If the sender is running one percent slower than the receiver, you'll hear a very brief gap of silence once every 48 seconds. If the sender is running one percent faster, you'll hear a slight stutter once every 48 seconds. In between those times, the audio should sound smooth and relatively normal, except that the pitch of the speaker's voice will be a little higher or lower than it should be.

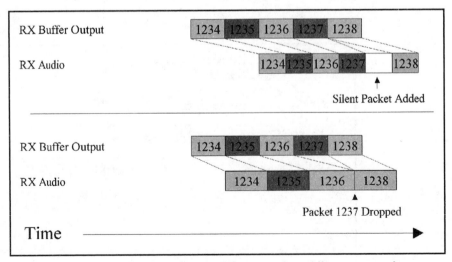

Figure 6.8—Compensating for timing differences by adding or removing packets.

ARCHITECTURE OF A SOUND CARD

A typical sound card is actually a combination of several devices: a waveform device, a musical synthesizer, a MIDI interface, and a pair of mixers. We'll focus on the two devices that are relevant to VoIP systems: the waveform device and the mixers.

Catch the Wave!

As we've already discussed, the waveform device captures digital samples of analog sound signals, and (in reverse) produces analog sound signals from digital samples. This is sometimes just called the *wave device*. Since it can work in both directions, there's a wave input and a wave output. The wave input takes sound from a microphone, or some other analog audio source, and digitizes it. The wave output takes digital audio and produces an analog audio signal from it, suitable for sending to a speaker or a radio transmitter.

The Mixers

A sound-card mixer is similar in concept to a mixing board you might find in a recording studio or radio station. The simplest kind of audio mixer isn't really a mixer at all, but a switch, which can route any one of several inputs to a single output. More commonly, a mixer combines two or more inputs into a single output, by adding, or *summing*, the signals together. With a set of potentiometers, the audio engineer can adjust the levels of each of the inputs to produce the desired result in the output.

A typical sound card actually contains *two* mixers. This causes some confusion for many computer users, but a look at **Figure 6.9** shows the reason why. One mixer combines each of the sound card's audio sources into the signal that goes to the speakers. This allows the speakers to be shared between the wave out, the music synthesizer, and even the microphone and line inputs.

The other mixer's job is to combine signals into the *input* of the waveform device, rather than working with the output. This is commonly called the recording mixer, or wave-input mixer. Again, the choices of audio sources include the microphone jack, the line-in jack, the music synthesizer, and sometimes even the first mixer's output.

In the innards of the *Windows* multimedia system, the components of a mixer are called *lines* and *controls*. Lines are sources or destinations of audio (called *source lines* and *destination lines*); controls determine how source lines are routed to destination lines, and in what quantities. The idea is that any mixing device, no matter how complex, can be represented by stringing combinations of lines and controls together, in Tinker Toy fash-

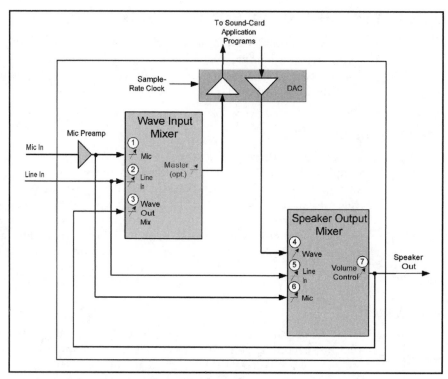

Figure 6.9—Simplified block diagram of a typical sound card. (Only the waveform audio paths are shown). The numbered volume controls correspond to the sliders shown in Figures 6.10 and 6.11.

Figure 6.10—A typical *Windows* playback **volume control panel. The numbered sliders correspond to the numbers in Figure 6.9. The appearance of this panel varies from one computer to another, depending on the particular sound card's capabilities. Also, not all of the available sliders are necessarily shown. On this particular computer, CD Player and Aux level controls were also available, but were not displayed because they had not been checked under Options—>Properties.**

ion. This way, manufacturers of sophisticated sound cards with dozens of inputs and outputs and all kinds of special effects can simply write drivers for their products, and they can be "dropped in" to work with nearly any existing *Windows* multimedia program.

Graphical Mixer Displays

An example of a program that works with these drivers is the volume-control applet found in the *Windows* Control Panel, usually called Sounds (or Sounds and Multimedia). It's also available by double-clicking the yellow loudspeaker icon in the *Windows* system tray (**Figure 6.10**).

On startup, the volume-control applet reads the electronic block diagram of the sound card's mixer(s), and displays each control as an appropriate clickable picture, such as a slider or a checkbox. The playback controls normally come up first, but you can switch to another set of controls, such as the recording controls (**Figure 6.11**), by making a selection from the Properties menu. Typically, the Playback controls correspond to the Speaker Out destination line, and the Recording controls correspond to the Wave Input destination line.

Why does this have to be so complicated? Why not just show three or four sliders, for microphone level, line-in level, and wave out level, for example? Hams who are working with sound-card software for the first time often ask this question. It's a fair question, but there are at least two reasons why it's done this way. The first is flexibility—some sound cards, for example, have no wave input at all; others have no wave output; others have no microphone line. Still others have a microphone line, but its level is fixed, not adjustable. The second reason is probably due to the way the sound card

Figure 6.11—A typical *Windows* recording volume control panel. The numbered sliders correspond to the numbers in Figure 6.9. To display this panel, open the Playback volume controls, then choose Recording from the Options—>Properties window. Just as with the playback controls, the type and number of sliders can vary. In this example, the Advanced button appears under the Microphone slider because the sound card has a "mic boost" option, *and* Advanced Controls was checked on the Options menu. Note also the Select check boxes. Although these are shown as check boxes rather than radio buttons, only one input can be selected at a time; some sound cards allow more than one to be selected.

is typically used. Unlike hams, I suspect that most *Windows* users are only interested in adjusting the levels going to the speakers—"turning the volume up and down." I'd guess that most *Windows* users have never plugged a microphone into their computer, and have no need to adjust the recording levels. So displaying recording level controls automatically might cause unnecessary confusion.

Incidentally, there's an undocumented shortcut for bringing up the Recording controls (instead of the Playback controls) directly. The volume-control applet is called *SNDVOL32.EXE*, and can be found in the *Windows* directory. If you're running *Windows 98* or above, you can go straight to the recording controls by typing

sndvol32 –r

at a command prompt, or creating a desktop shortcut to this command. This will display the Recording controls, as shown in Figure 6.11.

TRANSMIT-RECEIVE SWITCHING

The Internet, and most computer sound cards, work just fine in *full-duplex* mode—they can transmit and receive at the same time. Conventional radio transceivers, however, are not—they are inherently *half-duplex* devices; when they start transmitting, they stop receiving, and vice versa. In one sense, even a conventional 2-meter FM repeater isn't really a full-duplex device. Even though it transmits on one frequency while receiving on another, it can't process signals in both directions simultaneously, and stations using the repeater must take turns to transmit. Unlike telephone conversations, very few Amateur Radio conversations are full duplex.

What this means is that there must be a mechanism at each end of the Internet link to key the link radio on and off at the appropriate times. The link radio must only transmit when the station at the distant end of the Internet link has something to say, and then switch back to receive mode when the transmission is complete.

The two approaches commonly used for transmit-receiving switching are *carrier detect* (CD) and *voice-operated switch* (VOX).

CD is sometimes also called *carrier-operated switch* (COS) or *carrier-operated relay* (COR), because of its widespread use in FM repeaters to turn the repeater's transmitter on and off automatically. Typically, the receiver's squelch circuit is fitted with a special dc output which swings "high" only when the squelch is open (i.e., while a carrier is being received), and remains "low" at all other times. This allows external equipment, such as a repeater controller or a VoIP system, to detect the presence of a received signal.

VOX is familiar to anyone who has operated an SSB transceiver. When the operator begins speaking into the microphone, the rig starts transmitting. A second after the operator stops speaking, the rig stops transmitting. This is accomplished by a circuit that measures the peak voltage of the audio signal, compares it to a *threshold* voltage, and keys the transmitter if the peak exceeds the threshold. It also resets a timer that keeps the rig keyed for a second or two, to avoid switching between words. In much the same way, VOX can be used at the receiving end as a way of detecting a signal. Since it can be driven by the final audio stage of the receiver, it can be equally useful for FM as for SSB—as long as there's always some audio coming through. Unless it carries a CTCSS tone or background noise, a dead-carrier FM signal won't trigger an audio-based VOX.

Chapter 7

Under the Hood: *EchoLink*

EchoLink is designed to be easy to install, configure, and use, yet versatile enough to meet the needs of many different types of nodes. Although fairly simple on the outside, there's a lot happening on the inside during every contact.

The main components of the *EchoLink* software are shown in **Figure 7.1**. The program operates in either of two modes—*single-user mode* or *sysop mode*. The basic VoIP functions of both modes are the same, but sysop mode adds features to support a link transceiver or repeater connected to the PC.

Many of the components are familiar from our discussion of digital audio fundamentals. One of its key components is a digital audio mixer, which is used to combine audio signals from several sources (audio codec, Morse generator and speech generator) before sending them to the computer's sound card. *EchoLink* also includes several built-in digital signal-processing (DSP) functions, including a software-based DTMF decoder, which detects and decodes DTMF commands from the link transceiver.

EchoLink has several different input-output (I/O) functions. Of course, the program exchanges digitized voice data with the computer's sound card. But it also includes a user interface, which accepts commands from the keyboard and mouse and displays the program's status graphically. The program exchanges data with the PC's serial port to control the link equipment, and communicates with the Internet to exchange voice and text data with other stations and authentication and status information with the *EchoLink* servers. In sysop mode, a built-in Web server supports remote management of the node, and a program option sends status information to a TNC for distribution over the local APRS packet network.

One of the questions often asked about *EchoLink* is how the voice an-

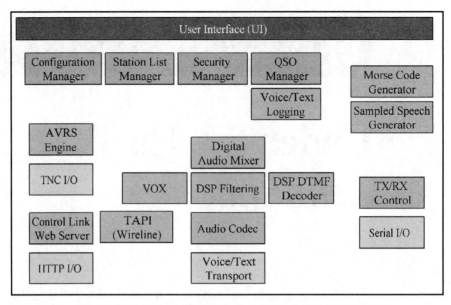

Figure 7.1—The major internal components of the *EchoLink* software.

nouncements are generated in sysop mode. Rather than being synthesized by a text-to-speech generator, the program actually contains short recordings (samples) of an actual voice (my own), and assembles them as needed to create announcements. There are about 50 samples built into the program, including the digits 0 through 9, the letters A through Z, and a short list of words and phrases.

SERVER ARCHITECTURE

EchoLink stations communicate directly with each other over the Internet. This kind of communication is called *peer-to-peer* because there is no master—all stations are on equal footing with each other. System engineers are fond of saying that this arrangement *scales* well, because it allows thousands and thousands of conversations to take place simultaneously, without creating a bottleneck at some central server.

If each *EchoLink* station kept its own list of every other *EchoLink* station it wanted to communicate with, along with a password (or some other form of authentication), no such central server would be required. However, there are many thousands of registered *EchoLink* stations, with more than 170 new ones coming online every day. Most of these stations use Internet providers that assign *dynamic addresses*, which means their Internet addresses change from time to time. Moreover, it's useful for each station to be able to keep running tabs as to who's online at a given moment, rather than simply keeping a big phone book around.

To meet all of these needs, the *EchoLink* system provides certain services to help get the conversation started. These services are as follows:

Authentication: Finding out who the user is—or making sure he is who he says he is.

Access control: Determining whether the user is allowed to access the system.

Discovery: Finding out who else is logged in to the system, to develop a list of active stations, and to keep track of each station's status.

Location: Keeping track of the Internet address of each station.

EchoLink uses a set of centralized servers, called *addressing servers*, to handle all four of these tasks (**Figure 7.2**). The addressing servers run silently behind the scenes 24 hours a day, and keep track of each station registered with *EchoLink*, which stations are currently logged in, and the

Figure 7.2—A simplified view of the *EchoLink* server architecture. Three addressing servers are shown. Note that the voice traffic between G3ABC and W1ABC (in this example) travels directly from station to station, and not through the servers.

Internet address (also called the *IP address*) of each station.

Why does this require more than one server? There are two good reasons: fault tolerance and scalability. The servers are arranged so that each one handles a share of the load—a technique known as *load balancing*. This arrangement also ensures that if one of the servers should fail, the others automatically pick up the slack by taking on an extra share of the load. In fact, two or three of the servers could be down, and the system would still work. Computers (and the Internet) being what they are, this is a welcome feature indeed.

Accomplishing this, however, requires some trickery. There are two sticky problems that must be solved: First, how is it that some *EchoLink* stations can contact one addressing server, and other stations contact another? And second, how can we ensure that no matter which addressing server they contact, each station can "see" the same information at the same time?

DNS To The Rescue!

Although there are several ways to balance load across several servers, one of the easiest ways is to take advantage of the Domain Name System, or DNS. DNS is the master telephone book of the Internet, the thing that translates an easy-to-remember name—like **www.arrl.org**—into a machine-friendly address—like 216.167.96.124. One of the useful features of DNS is its ability to associate more than one IP address with a single name, a little bit like having several different phone numbers in the same household. This type of DNS listing can be set up so that every time the *EchoLink* software requests the IP address of an addressing server, the DNS server spits back a different answer. This mechanism, known as *round-robin load balancing*, is an easy way to send an equal number of requests to any of several different servers, no matter where in the world they are located.

Another useful feature of DNS is just the opposite—the ability to associate more than one name with a single address. These additional names, sometimes called *aliases*, make it possible for a single server to assume multiple identities.

How does this benefit *EchoLink*? When the software is installed, *EchoLink* examines the prefix of your call sign to determine in which country you're likely to be located, by consulting the official ITU prefix list. Based on the name of the country (and, in some cases, the numbered call area within the country), the software assembles a list of the addressing servers most likely to be closest to you geographically. These names are **naeast.echolink.org** for the Eastern part of North America, **nawest.echolink.org** for the Western part, **asia.echolink.org** for Asia, and so forth. The last item in the list is always the generic name **servers.echolink.org**.

This is where DNS steps in. Each of these names is actually an alias rather than a true server name. And although there are six or seven such aliases, there are typically only three or four addressing servers active, so many of these names "point" to the same physical server. Finally, the generic name **servers.echolink.org** has all four physical server addresses associated with it, in the round-robin fashion described above.

What makes this technique attractive is that the *EchoLink* system administrators can adjust the load on each of the addressing servers, to some extent, by changing the way the DNS aliases are assigned. Another nice feature is that the *EchoLink* software will always find a "live" server, regardless of how the list of servers had been assembled. All servers are listed under **servers.echolink.org**, and the *EchoLink* software is designed to work its way through each IP address in the list until it succeeds. Thanks to this design, the *EchoLink* system has remained up and running despite all sorts of hardware, software, and Internet catastrophes (which, fortunately, are now rare).

Replication

The second problem is a little thornier. If W1XYZ is logged in to Server 1, and W6XYZ is logged in to Server 2, how will W1XYZ and W6XYZ ever find out about each other, so they can have a chat? Clearly, there needs to be some way for the two severs to "talk" to each other so that they know about each other's logins. This sort of electronic chatter is called *replication*. Every 20 seconds, each of the addressing servers asks each of the other servers, "Pardon me, but who has logged in (or logged off) since the last time I asked?" (Large, expensive computers are exceptionally polite.) The other server responds with a list of all the changes since the last time that question was asked (i.e., in the past 20 seconds), and so Server 1 has an exact snapshot of what's happening on Server 2.

By asking only for the differences, not the whole list, the conversation takes up a minimal amount of bandwidth. This is an important design feature when you consider how often these exchanges must take place. If four addressing servers are active, each server is asking each of the other three servers for updates every 20 seconds—an average of one question every seven seconds.

Wouldn't it be more efficient to just broadcast a message to all servers each time a station logs in or logs off? Not when you consider how many transactions the addressing servers are handling. As a group, the servers process about one million transactions every 24 hours, an average of 11 transactions per second. By exchanging this information in 20-second batches, each set of changes can be sent in a single, compact package.

AUTHENTICATION AND VALIDATION

The final piece of the puzzle is security, which is an important factor in any Internet-based application. Certainly, Amateur Radio is not particularly secure—no one asks for proof of license or a password when you turn on your rig—but there is heightened sensitivity to security on the Internet because personal computers are in the hands of so many millions of users worldwide, only a small fraction of whom are licensed Amateur Radio operators.

Some of the important aspects of Internet security are authentication, access control, data integrity, and privacy. We've defined authentication and access control already. Data integrity deals with making sure the message hasn't been tampered with since the original sender sent it; privacy deals with making sure no one else can eavesdrop on the conversation.

EchoLink's security model focuses on authentication and access control. The first step is *validation*, which is the process of registering a new brand new user who has just installed the software. The main purpose of validation is to ensure that each user of *EchoLink* is a duly licensed Amateur Radio operator, and if so, to associate a password with his call sign. This process is described in detail in the next section.

Once validated, the user's call sign and password are stored in a database on a special server called the *validation server*. Slimmed-down copies of this database are also kept on each of the addressing servers. Each *EchoLink* user's software must provide his call sign and the matching password to the addressing server before being allowed access. Only after the addressing server has verified the password will the user be logged in, and only after logging in will the *EchoLink* software allow connections to be made to other stations. Furthermore, the *EchoLink* software at the other end will only *accept* connections from stations that are duly logged in, as verified by the addressing server. This two-way security mechanism is particularly efficient since it doesn't require any information to be stored at each *EchoLink* user's computer, except the user's own call sign and password. In effect, each *EchoLink* user's software is delegating authentication to the central server, rather than having to manage it on its own. This kind of *trust-based* authentication is common in many computer systems, particularly those on corporate networks.

However, the *EchoLink* software does allow individual users to make their own access-control rules, over and above basic authentication. You can say, for example, that only stations from Côte D'Ivoire and Finland are allowed to access your link. You can build a list of specific call signs that are to be denied access, or you can limit access to a short list of call signs that are allowed during a special net session. In this way, individual users can make their own rules about access control, while still delegating authentication to the servers.

What about privacy? Certainly, many transactions on the Internet need to be private, and the messages sent back and forth are sometimes encrypted. When you use your credit card to buy books, or connect to your company's extranet to learn about the bonus plan, you want some assurance that no one else could be eavesdropping on the conversation. Such is not the case with Amateur Radio, however. Conversations on the air are never private (in fact, FCC rules prohibit using codes or encryption to obscure the meaning of a transmission), so there really isn't a compelling need to ensure the privacy of Internet-linked Amateur Radio communication. Although VoIP data *could* be encrypted, the systems described in this book do not do so, thus saving computer CPU cycles for other tasks.

Validating New Users

None of these security mechanisms are very helpful if there isn't a reliable way to screen new users, to be sure they are indeed licensed amateurs, and using the call sign that's been assigned to them.

This is where authentication steps in once again. Recall that authentication is the process of ensuring that "you are who you say you are." FCC records might be very clear that WJ2MS is a person named Joseph M. Schmo who lives in Schmoville, NJ, and is an Extra Class licensee whose ticket expires in 2011. But when someone says "I'm WJ2MS; please validate me for *EchoLink*," how do we know it's the real Joe Schmo, and not his evil twin?

Clearly, we need to have something akin to showing a driver's license when you cash a check. If you walk into a supermarket for the first time and whip out your checkbook in the express lane, the cashier will probably ask you to authenticate yourself by asking for some form of ID. If it's a store you visit every week, you can probably get a check-cashing card, which is a form of ID issued by the supermarket itself, and thus minimize the grumbling of all the people in line behind you.

As you have probably guessed, a good way to prove your identity as a ham is to produce a copy of your amateur license. This is exactly what the *EchoLink* administrators request from many new users, dozens of times each day. A special e-mail address and fax number have been set up so that new users can scan or copy their license, and send the copy to *EchoLink* for review. Once examined, the call sign is marked "validated" on the *EchoLink* servers, and the password that had originally been selected by the new user becomes his key to identify himself each time he logs in.

The *EchoLink* administrators, who work around the clock in several different time zones, also have at their disposal specially-designed tools for managing the user database, incoming e-mail, tracking logs, and international call sign databases, all as part of the validation process. A number of countries, such as the United States, Canada, Brazil, Japan and France offer downloadable or searchable databases of Amateur Radio license records.

The *EchoLink* back-end system maintains local *mirrors* (copies) of some of these databases to further cross-check validation requests, such as ensuring that the requestor's license has not already expired or been cancelled.

But today *EchoLink*, and tomorrow perhaps *MegaLink*, and *DXLink*, and *5By9Link*. As more and more Internet-based Amateur Radio applications emerge, will each one require its users (and administrators) to go through the same gyrations, in order to ensure security?

Fortunately, the answer is "no". Just as the check-cashing card is to the supermarket chain, the *digital certificate* is to the Amateur Radio Service. The idea is that a ham should only have to authenticate herself once to some trusted organization, and from then on, just present her digital ID card to anyone else who needs it.

In September 2003, the ARRL inaugurated its *Logbook of the World* (LoTW) program. LoTW is an Internet-based system for submitting entries from your logbook, in order to verify contacts and qualify for awards such as WAS and DXCC. Like an electronic QSL card, an entry is considered valid if both you and the other station have reported the same contact to LoTW.

Critical to the success of LoTW is strong authentication. If you want to participate in LoTW, you request a digital certificate from the ARRL. The ARRL staff then authenticates you, either by asking you for copies of documentation, or by sending a postcard with a special code to your registered mailing address. Once you're authenticated, you receive a signed digital certificate (by e-mail), and you're ready to submit log entries to LoTW.

Like an ATM card, you can't use a digital certificate to prove your identity unless you know the secret *private key*, or at least have access to it. This is analogous to the PIN for your ATM card. Usually, your private key is stored on your computer, and kept locked up with a password. The matching *public key* is stored in the digital certificate itself, which you can freely give out to anyone who needs to authenticate you.

To prove your identity, you "sign" a message with your private key, and then send the message, the electronic signature and the digital certificate to the person who needs it. That person then verifies the signature by using the public key to decrypt it, and checking to be sure the signature matches the message, and that the certificate is valid. If everything checks out, he can be sure it was you who sent it.

This sounds like quite a long process, but it can all be done in a fraction of a second by computers at both ends of the conversation. In fact, it's exactly what happens when you visit a secure Web site with your Web browser, except that the roles are reversed—the Web site is authenticating itself to you.

The best part is that once you have this digital certificate, you can use it as an electronic ID card for other Amateur Radio systems that are set up to accept it. Among those that do is *EchoLink*. As an alternative to submitting a photocopy of your license, *EchoLink* provides a special utility that will generate a validation request, sign it, and send it (along with your digital certificate) to the *EchoLink* servers. If the signature is verified at the other end, you've been authenticated successfully. Quite a bit easier than sending a copy of your license!

At the heart of this arrangement is *trust*. In effect, *EchoLink* trusts the ARRL to properly verify the identity of each user to whom it provides a digital certificate. The certificate itself is signed by the ARRL, which in this scenario is acting as the *certification authority* (CA). Currently, the ARRL is the only CA that *EchoLink* recognizes, but there may be other organizations added to this list in the future. In this example, *EchoLink* is not a CA, just another party in the transaction.

Logging In

Once a call sign has been validated for use with *EchoLink*, its password is stored alongside the call sign in the master *user database*, and distributed to the cached database at each regional addressing server. When the new user starts up the *EchoLink* software a second time, the software "logs in" to one of the addressing servers by providing this call sign and password.

However, to avoid sending the password "in the clear" over the Internet, the password is encrypted. Enter public-key cryptography once again! Each addressing server has a public key. On startup, the *EchoLink* software requests the server's public key and a challenge phrase—a random, unique string of characters concocted each time by the server. Using the server's public key, the *EchoLink* software then encrypts both the password and the challenge phrase, and sends this encrypted message to the server. The server decrypts the message with its private key, and then verifies that both the challenge phrase and the password are correct. If so, the user's call sign is marked as "logged in", and his node can begin connecting to other stations in the *EchoLink* system.

VOX CONTROL

EchoLink has an optional, built-in VOX (an acronym for "voice operated switch") that can be used in Sysop mode to detect a signal on the receiver. Although it's implemented in software rather than hardware, it functions very much like the VOX circuit in an SSB transceiver. When the peak (sampled) voltage of the audio input reaches a certain threshold, the VOX is triggered and engaged, and a timer is started. When the timer expires, the VOX is released.

VOX might seem like a poor choice for detecting the presence of FM signals, but it can give reasonably good results in situations where a more positive, direct method of carrier detect is unavailable or impractical. For example, it's commonly used when the link receiver is tuned to the output frequency of a repeater. Most repeaters have a "tail" of 5 or 10 seconds during which the carrier remains on after the last transmission ceases. In this situation, a VOX can distinguish between a voice signal and a dead carrier, whereas a direct carrier-detect circuit cannot.

However, there are several problems with this technique. One problem is that if the VOX is adjusted to ignore a dead carrier, it might also drop out during a pause between sentences, giving a remote station the impression that it's now his turn to transmit.

A second problem is that other audio signals, such as squelch tails and noise bursts, will also trigger the VOX. This is clearly undesirable for an Internet link, which is inherently half-duplex. For example, even if the "anti-thump" or "pulseback" timer is adjusted so that the link receiver ignores its own squelch tail, the *repeater's* squelch tail is heard 5 to 10 seconds later. Ideally, a VOX could be made "smart" so that it ignored these non-voice signals.

EchoLink has just such a feature. It can be enabled in Sysop mode by engaging an option called Squelch Crash Anti-Trip (SCAT). Using digital signal processing techniques and a digital delay line, when properly adjusted, it will cause *EchoLink*'s VOX to ignore short bursts of noise.

Figure 7.3 shows the audio envelope of the end of a typical transmission from a repeater, as seen by a link receiver tuned to the repeater's output. Note that the courtesy tone and the squelch tail each have a characteristic signature: a short burst of noise surrounded on both sides by silence.

Figure 7.4 shows how the Smart VOX works. After sampling and digitizing the incoming audio, it is placed into a queue—a digital delay line. A representation of the signal's envelope is obtained by passing the signal through a digital low-pass filter. The program examines the envelope, compares the peak amplitude to the VOX threshold, and checks the amplitude of the signal immediately before and after it in time. The VOX is triggered only if the signal doesn't match the characteristics of a noise burst. At the end of the delay line, the audio is passed through to the Internet transport. The delay line ensures that no part of the signal is clipped by the VOX due to its delayed triggering.

REMOTE CONTROL

Fortunately, many countries (with some notable exceptions) currently do not require that stations running as Internet voice gateways have a control operator sitting in front of the radio. Instead, the rules allow link stations to be operated under either *automatic control* or *remote control*. (For a more complete discussion, see the chapter "Legal Issues").

Figure 7.3—Audio envelope of a typical signal received from an FM repeater.

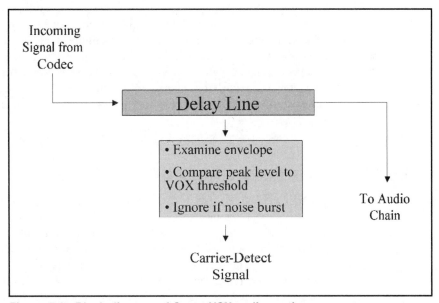

Figure 7.4—Block diagram of Smart VOX audio routing.

There are two ways to perform remote control of a link station: over an RF link, or over a wireline link. *EchoLink* has built-in features to support three types of control links:

RF control. Linking interfaces (and multi-purpose interfaces) for *EchoLink* usually have a second audio input, for connecting a control receiver (such as a UHF receiver). The audio from the control receiver is routed into the DTMF decoder on the board, but not into the audio path that feeds the computer's sound card. This allows a control operator to send DTMF commands over a control link frequency without the commands being heard over the air.

Internet control. *EchoLink* has a simple, built-in Web server that hosts a single, master control page. When properly configured, the control link can be accessed from any Internet Web browser in the world, given the right security credentials. From this page, the control operator can enable or disable the link, connect or disconnect a station, and view the recent status log.

Dial-in control. If the PC is equipped with a "voice modem", such as the type used for PC-based telephone answering machines, *EchoLink* has an option that allows a control operator to dial in from a touch-tone telephone and enter DTMF commands to control the link, without the commands being heard over the air. This feature is similar to the telephone-line control available on some repeater controllers. The control op can also hear the transmitted or received audio over the dial-in connection.

Even though radio regulations may require that a wireline or RF control link be in place when an Internet voice gateway is operating, it doesn't necessarily imply that *all* control functions must be performed over this link. More often, it is used as a backup in case the primary input frequency of the link is busy or otherwise unreachable. For example, you might normally disconnect the link by sending a DTMF pound sign (#) over the gateway's input frequency, but you would have to use the wireline or RF control link to disconnect the link if it's connected to a long-winded roundtable conversation and none of the stations is leaving a long enough pause to let the VOX drop.

SCRIPTING AND AUTOMATION

After using the *EchoLink* software, if you're like most enterprising amateurs, it won't be long before you'll be thinking of ways it could be improved or extended. Plenty of features and configuration options are included in the program, but it would be impossible (or at least, impractical) to try to cram in every imaginable bell and whistle. Some programs suffer from a malady called *Featureitis* when the whole kitchen sink is thrown in.

Fortunately, *EchoLink* is extendable. Like many *Windows* programs, it includes an *Automation interface*, which is a mechanism by which other programs (or scripts) can interact with it under the covers. Virtually all of the program's functions and options can be controlled this way, and *EchoLink* can also fire *event notifications* when significant things happen, such as another station connecting to yours. This opens up plenty of possibilities for automating or enhancing *EchoLink*.

Automation is part of the component object model (COM) specification championed by Microsoft. In the COM Automation paradigm, clients control servers, and servers can send event notifications to clients. In this context, a "server" is just a program (or a piece of a program) that provides something useful to other programs. You can think of *EchoLink* as a COM server that provides amateur VoIP linking services to other programs on your computer.

Client programs can be written in any programming language or scripting language that supports COM. The most popular language for COM clients is probably Visual Basic. If you've had any experience writing *Visual Basic* programs, interfacing with *EchoLink* will be a snap, since COM Automation is fully baked into the VB environment. *C++* developers familiar with COM will also find an easy fit (in fact, *EchoLink* itself was developed in the *C++* programming language). COM components can also be accessed from the .NET environment, with languages such as *C#*.

Another option is to write a client program using a scripting language. The VBScript and Jscript languages are built into every *Windows* computer, but it's also possible to write client programs in *Perl* or *Python* after installing the appropriate engine. Scripting languages are a good choice for quick-and-dirty tasks that don't require a user interface, such as starting or stopping *EchoLink*, or commanding it to connect or disconnect according to a schedule.

Several VBScript examples are installed along with the *EchoLink* software, including examples of scripts that receive events from *EchoLink* and respond to them. Complete details of the COM interface, also called the API, are available in the *EchoLink* Programmer's Guide, which can be downloaded from the *EchoLink* Web site.

With some imagination and a modicum of programming skill, you can create programs or scripts that:

• Enable or disable *EchoLink* (in Sysop mode) according to a schedule. Use *Windows* Task Scheduler to run either an "Enable" script or a "Disable" script at pre-set times.

• Connect to specific stations in response to other events. For example, you could create a script that conferences-in W1XYZ each time W2XXX connects.

• Extend the existing set of DTMF commands. Each DTMF string received by *EchoLink*'s decoder fires an Automation event. Your program can receive this event and take appropriate action. This could be used, for example, to control other devices connected to the PC.

• Extend the remote Web control capabilities, in Sysop mode. *EchoLink*'s built-in Web server is very basic, but you can create your own Web interface (using Web server software) that provides many more features and functions.

A few real-world script examples are shown in this chapter. The example in **Figure 7.5** is a VBScript script that runs in the *Windows* Scripting Host environment (*cscript.exe*), and takes advantage of WSH's support for Automation events.

The example in **Figure 7.6** is a short *Perl* program that connects to *EchoLink* using the Win32 OLE module shipped with ActiveState's *ActivePerl*. (It is also possible to use WSH with a PerlScript script; see the ActiveState documentation for more information.)

Figure 7.7 is a *C++* version of the Perl program in Figure 7.6. It uses the *#import* technique (supported by Visual Studio) to generate a set of smart-pointer classes from *EchoLink*'s type library.

These are just a few examples as food for thought. If you're a little rusty on COM programming, consult one of the many books on the subject. *Visual Basic 6* (or *Visual Studio .NET*) is probably the easiest development tool with which to get started writing companion programs for *EchoLink*.

LOCAL CONTROL IN SYSOP MODE

Many stations running *EchoLink* as an RF gateway (i.e., with a -L or -R suffix) have the computer located in the shack, or in some other easy-to-reach location. It would seem natural to be able to use the link using a microphone plugged into the PC's sound card, rather than having to pick up an HT just to answer a call or join a conversation in progress.

Fortunately, there is a feature in *EchoLink* that allows you to do just that. With the right hardware and software settings, you can use a local microphone alongside the RF gear, and when you transmit, you'll be heard by the remotely connected station (over the Internet) as well as over your own RF link.

The key is to connect the PC microphone to the Microphone jack of your PC's sound card, and connect the audio from the link receiver to the Line-In jack. This allows *EchoLink* to switch between the two inputs on the fly.

Here are the other steps:

• Set your *Windows* Recording Volume controls so that *both* the Line and Microphone inputs are turned up to normal levels. *EchoLink* will use the Mute or Select controls to switch between the two.

• On your *Windows* Playback Volume control panel, turn up the Micro-

```
'ConnectWhenReady.vbs: Wait until the specified station comes online, then
connect to it.

'Author: Jonathan Taylor, K1RFD
'Date: July 23, 2003

'To invoke this script from the command line, type:
'       cscript ConnectWhenReady.vbs call sign
'where "call sign" is the call sign of the station to which to connect.
'This script should only be run if EchoLink is already running.


If WScript.Arguments.Count > 0 Then

        sStation = UCase(WScript.Arguments(0))

        'Instantiate EchoLink's Session component, and set up an event
connection
        Set oEchoLink = WScript.CreateObject("EchoLink.EchoLinkSession",
"EchoLink_")

        'get a fresh copy of the station list to kick things off
        'oEchoLink.RefreshStationList True

        'is the desired station already online?
        If IsStationOnlineAndNotBusy(sStation) Then
                oEchoLink.Connect sStation, True
                WScript.Quit(0)
        Else
                'sleep and let events drive things from now on
                WScript.Echo "Sleeping..."
                While True
                        WScript.Sleep 1000
                Wend
        End If
End If

Sub EchoLink_Closing
        'EchoLink is shutting down; exit now to avoid picking daisies
        WScript.DisconnectObject(oEchoLink)
        Set oEchoLink = Nothing
        WScript.Quit(0)
End Sub


Sub EchoLink_StationListReceived

        'This event fires each time the Station List is refreshed.
        'Check the revised station list
        'for the desired call sign; go back to sleep if not found.

        If IsStationOnlineAndNotBusy(sStation) Then
                oEchoLink.Connect sStation, True
                WScript.Quit(0)
        End If
End Sub
```

Figure 7.5—A VBScript example, including event hooks.

```
#! .perl

#Connect.pl: Attempt to connect EchoLink to the specified station.

#Author: Jonathan Taylor, K1RFD
#Date: December 3, 2003

#To invoke this script from the command line, type:
#       perl Connect.pl call sign
#where "call sign" is the call sign of the station to which to connect.


use strict;
use Win32::OLE;
my $el = Win32::OLE->new('EchoLink.EchoLinkSession');

#get a fresh copy of the station list; also ensures that
#   EchoLink is fully initialized
$el->RefreshStationList(1);

#attempt the connect
my $station = uc($ARGV[0]);
$el->Connect($station, 1);

#check the results
my $bConnected = $el->IsPeerConnected($station);
if ($bConnected ) {
        print "Connect succeeded.";
} else {
        print "Connect failed.";
}
```

Figure 7.6—A *Perl* example.

phone slider. This allows audio from the microphone to travel to the audio input of your RF link transmitter. (If you have PC speakers connected, you might need to turn down their volume a bit to avoid feedback). *EchoLink* will use the Mute control, if available, to switch the microphone on and off.

• In *EchoLink*, under Tools->Sysop Settings, choose the TX Ctrl tab and check the box marked "Key PTT On Local Transmit". This will key the link transmitter whenever you "key" *EchoLink*'s TX, such as by pressing the space bar.

• Under Tools->Preferences, choose the Connections tab, click "PTT Control", and check the box marked "Auto-Select Mic Input". This will switch the Recording mixer over to Microphone input when you TX locally, instead of taking the link receiver's audio from Line-In.

If you are running in Sysop mode, it's also possible to connect a local push-to-talk switch to your computer's serial port. This would be a natural arrangement if your local microphone is a communications-type mic with a built-in PTT switch. Here are the additional steps:

```cpp
// ELConnect.cpp: Attempt to connect EchoLink to the specified station.

// Author: Jonathan Taylor, K1RFD
// Date: December 3, 2003

#include <windows.h>
#include <stdio.h>

#import "\Program Files\K1RFD\EchoLink\EchoLink.exe" no_namespace

int main(int argc, char* argv[])
{
        CoInitialize(NULL);

        IEchoLinkSessionPtr pEL;
        HRESULT hr = pEL.CreateInstance(__uuidof(EchoLinkSession));
        if (SUCCEEDED(hr)) {

                try {

                        // get a fresh copy of the station list; also ensures
that
                        // EchoLink is fully initialized
                        pEL->RefreshStationList(VARIANT_TRUE);

                        // attempt the connect
                        _bstr_t sStation = argv[1];
                        pEL->Connect(sStation, VARIANT_TRUE);

                        // check the results
                        VARIANT_BOOL bConnected = pEL-
>IsPeerConnected(sStation);

                        if (bConnected) {
                                printf("Connect succeeded.\n");
                        } else {
                                printf("Connect failed.\n");
                        }
                } catch (_com_error e) {
                        printf("Error: %s\n", (char *)e.Description());
                }

        }

        CoUninitialize();

        return 0;
}
```

Figure 7.7—A _C++_ example.

 • Connect the push-to-talk switch to the COM port connector in such a way that the CTS pin goes high (or low) when you press the button, or vice versa. A typical arrangement is to connect the PTT switch between CTS and ground (pins 8 and 5 on a DB-9 connector) and then pull the CTS pin normally high with a resistor to a 5-12V dc power source. When the switch is

```
2003-12-18 16:55:11 2003-12-18 17:08:00 W1CDM-R     CONF            SAN DIEGO, CA
2003-12-18 18:57:38 2003-12-18 18:59:38 G0MEJ        Nigel P         NW Eng (1)
2003-12-18 20:18:20 2003-12-18 20:19:25 N9TEV        Jeffrey Geiger  Antigo wi 54409
2003-12-18 20:38:30 2003-12-18 20:38:43 VU3GTF       KARAN           NEW DELHI , INDIA (1)
2003-12-18 21:05:10 2003-12-18 21:09:09 KA2LOG-L     CONF            New Rochelle, NY (1)
2003-12-18 21:16:22 2003-12-18 21:17:34 KC2MHA       Tommy           Staten Island, NY
2003-12-18 21:35:36 2003-12-18 21:38:27 N1LRC        Randy           East Bridgewater Ma.
2003-12-18 22:10:36 2003-12-18 22:12:22 KF4OHI-L     Charles         Houston, TX.   USA
2003-12-18 22:14:10 2003-12-18 22:16:23 KF4OHI-L     CONF            Houston, TX.   USA
2003-12-18 22:24:06 2003-12-18 22:25:41 KB2DY        Pete            Massapequa, New York
```

Figure 7.8—A portion of an *EchoLink* Call sign log file.

```
2003-12-19 08:21:23 Connect WA2TQI-L          BILL 9626 141.150.204.138
2003-12-19 08:22:27 Disconnect WA2TQI-L Peer requested disconnect
2003-12-19 09:33:34 DTMFCommand 01
2003-12-19 09:33:38 Connect LU5ACJ-L          JUAN 27949 24.232.82.61
2003-12-19 09:35:00 DTMFCommand #
2003-12-19 09:35:00 Disconnect LU5ACJ-L DTMF Disconnect command
2003-12-19 10:25:49 Connect IT9GUO            Massimo 155661 151.38.65.153
2003-12-19 10:27:23 Disconnect IT9GUO Peer requested disconnect
2003-12-19 11:49:58 Connect WA1APP            David L. 79444 172.208.53.245
2003-12-19 11:50:24 Disconnect WA1APP Peer requested disconnect
2003-12-19 12:22:12 Verifying WT1I            donald Ridley 68.101.77.115
2003-12-19 12:22:17 Connect WT1I              donald Ridley - 68.101.77.115
2003-12-19 12:24:05 Disconnect WT1I Peer requested disconnect
2003-12-19 13:12:42 Connect KE4BHA            Robert Batten 113452
216.76.211.192
2003-12-19 13:13:33 Disconnect KE4BHA Peer requested disconnect
```

Figure 7.9—A portion of an *EchoLink* System log file.

pressed, the CTS pin goes low.

• Under Tools->Preferences, choose the Connections tab, click "PTT Control", and check the box marked "Serial Port CTS". Then, choose the correct COM port, and check the box marked "Active Low" if the CTS pin goes low on transmit, rather than high.

• Verify the configuration by connecting to the Test Server and ensuring that *EchoLink* goes into TX whenever the PTT button is pressed.

LOGGING

EchoLink has several logging features that provide useful historical information about usage of the link.

Call sign log: This is a text file with one line for each contact, including the date, time, call sign, and description of each station to which your node has connected. The log entry is recorded at the moment the station disconnects. This log is the closest equivalent to a typical amateur station log file, and is in a format that can be easily imported into spreadsheets or logging programs. A portion of a typical Call sign log is shown in **Figure 7.8**.

System log: The System log records all important information about operation of the link, such as stations connecting and disconnecting, DTMF codes received, and startup and shutdown of the link itself. A portion of a typical System log is shown in **Figure 7.9**.

Sound files: *EchoLink* has an option to "tape record" contacts that take place over the link, providing the ultimate record of what was said, when it was said, and by whom. When this option is enabled, *EchoLink* stores all incoming and outgoing audio signals as WAV files. These files can be played back at any time in the future using a utility such as *Windows Media Player*. Depending on the settings, *EchoLink* will either record each transmission as a separate file (tagged with the call sign of the sender), or put all transmissions in a single conversation together as a larger file. In either mode, it automatically removes periods of silence, to keep the files small and to make it easier to review them.

Chapter 8

Under the Hood: *IRLP*

IRLP is a collection of scripts, configuration files and executable programs (called *binaries*) that work closely together. One of the strengths of the system is its flexibility. Small pieces of the system be updated as needed, and enterprising node owners can do a great deal of customization by modifying (or adding) scripts or binaries themselves.

The heart of the node software is the *Linux* implementation of the open-source VoIP program *Speak Freely*. *Speak Freely* handles the basic tasks in the lowest level of the voice-over-Internet conversation, such as the UDP transport, buffering, compression and decompression, and management of the audio device (the sound card). The other programs and scripts are what make *IRLP* custom-engineered for Amateur Radio linking. These include programs that interact with the interface board (to operate the link transceiver and detect DTMF digits), and other *daemons* that run in the background to process connection requests and software updates. There is also a set of utility programs and scripts for testing the system and performing certain tasks manually, from the *Linux* command shell.

Although *IRLP* can be set up on an existing *Linux* installation, it's most commonly installed along with a custom distribution of *Linux* on a "clean" machine. There are two advantages to setting up *IRLP* this way: First, by installing *IRLP* and *Linux* at the same time from the same distribution, you can be sure the two are compatible versions of software that are designed to work together. Second, the *Linux* install shipped with the *IRLP* kit installs only the components of *Linux* that are required for *IRLP*, without unnecessary extras. This is particularly important if you are resurrecting an older PC for use as an *IRLP* machine, and want to make maximum use of the available hardware resources, such as disk space and RAM.

HARDWARE ARCHITECTURE

The only specialized hardware used by *IRLP* is the *IRLP* interface board (see Chapter 5, Figure 5.1). The interface board, which is provided by *IRLP* as part of the hardware/software kit, ties together the PC's parallel port, the input/output jacks of the sound card, and the link transceiver (or repeater). The board contains a DTMF decoder chip, and additional components for detecting the COS signal from the receiver and keying the PTT line of the transmitter. It uses the PC's parallel port to exchange commands and data with the software.

The board also provides three general-purpose auxiliary output pins which can be keyed on and off from the software. These are normally open MOSFET outputs that can be switched to ground. For example, a custom DTMF script could be written that enables or disables a secondary receiver in response to commands sent over the link frequency.

The *SpeakFreely* module must (of course) communicate with the PC's sound card, and one of the *IRLP* hardware requirements is that a genuine Sound Blaster sound card be used. The *IRLP* Web site carries a complete list of the various Sound Blaster models that have been tested. Fortunately, the list of sound-card drivers for *Linux* is growing rapidly, and so may the list of supported sound cards. Creative Labs has released dozens of Sound Blaster models over the years, so finding a compatible sound card for your machine shouldn't be a problem.

GETTING CONNECTED

An *IRLP* conversation begins when a station in range of one node, call it Node A, punches in the four-digit node number of the station he'd like to connect to, using his DTMF pad. These tones are picked up by the node's link transceiver, and passed along to the audio input of the *IRLP* interface board. The board's DTMF decoder chip detects the dual-tone signals, converts them the corresponding binary values (representing 0, 1, A, #, etc.) and sends them to the parallel port. *IRLP*'s DTMF program accepts this data from the parallel port and passes it as a string of ASCII digits to a script, which interprets the digits according to a list of rules.

If the script determines that this is a "connect" command (normally a four-digit sequence), it starts the process of locating the remote station and connecting to it over the Internet.

The first step in this process is to determine the remote node's IP address. Since IP addresses frequently change, the software consults a special DNS server to learn under which address this particular node is logged in. *IRLP* operates a set of several name servers that work as backups to each other. Even if no server is reachable for some reason, the software automatically falls back to a cached copy of the list in a local **hosts** file.

Once the IP address is determined, communication between the nodes begins. The first order of business is a special message sent from Node A to Node B saying, in effect, "I'd like to connect to you—please respond." If Node B is open for business, it will have a program running in the background that is listening for connection requests such as this, and the request will be received and processed.

Now that the two nodes know that they want to connect to each other, they begin by authenticating each other. Each node has a copy of *IRLP*'s PGP *keyring*—the list of each node's public key—and, of course, its own private key. Using PGP (explained in detail in the next section), and a challenge-response conversation in both directions, Node A and Node B each assure themselves that the other is legitimate.

Before firing up the VoIP link, there's one more order of business—to decide on a codec. *IRLP* supports both GSM and ADPCM. Although ADPCM is the default, if the calling node is configured to run GSM, the answering node will need to use GSM, too.

Finally, both stations start up their *Speak Freely* software, and now can begin exchanging VoIP signals. The conversation has begun!

During the conversation, the two nodes alternate between sending and receiving streams of VoIP packets. When the *IRLP* software on Node A detects an active COS signal, it tells *Speak Freely* to begin encoding audio from the sound card and shipping it off as a chain of packets to Node B over the Internet. The *Speak Freely* software on Node B, which has been eagerly awaiting the arrival of these packets, receives the first one in the chain and tells the *IRLP* software to key up the local link via PTT. Each incoming packet is parsed, decompressed and sent to the sound card for playback. When the COS signal at Node A finally drops, the flow of packets ceases, and Node B releases PTT after a short delay.

The virtual connection between Node A and Node B remains "up" until one node or the other drops it, or until one node or the other stops responding. (This can happen if the Internet connection fails in the middle of a conversation.) Separately from the raw VoIP data, the nodes send *keep-alive* messages to each other periodically to be sure the other side is still able to respond.

PRETTY GOOD PRIVACY (PGP)

One of the lynchpins of *IRLP*'s security system is a mechanism called PGP, or Pretty Good Privacy. PGP is a data-security technique that can provide data privacy, integrity and authentication. It's commonly used to prepare messages that move over the Internet from one computer to another, since none of these features is inherent in the Internet itself.

PGP uses two ingenious techniques for making this work. The first is called *public-key cryptography*. This is a method of encrypting a message so that the sender and receiver can keep its contents private, without the sender and receiver having agreed upon a *key* ahead of time. The second, which is related to it, is called *digital signing*—a way of verifying a message using a digital signature.

In cryptography, a key is somewhat like a password; given an encrypted message, the recipient can unlock (decrypt) the message if he knows the right key. Often, the same key is used to encrypt the message as to decrypt it. However, mathematicians have discovered that it's possible to create two completely different keys that work as a pair—one is used to encrypt the message, and the other is used to decrypt it. This is called a public-private key pair, because one key is usually freely advertised, while the other one is kept secret.

Here's how it works: The recipient of a message has a public-private key pair. Someone who wants to send him a message first asks him for his public key, which he freely gives out. The sender then uses the public key to encrypt a message, and sends the encrypted message to the recipient. After getting the message, the recipient decrypts it using his private key. Anyone who might have intercepted the message on its way to the recipient won't be able to make heads or tails of it, because the only way to decrypt it is to use the private key, which the recipient has kept secret.

Public-key cryptography requires a lot of number crunching, however, and long messages might take a long time for a computer to encrypt. So instead, public-key techniques are often used to help the sender and receiver securely exchange a shorter key that's used to encrypt and decrypt the actual message.

If this sounds like a lot of effort to go through, you might be surprised to learn that it happens every time you visit a "secure" Internet site with your Web browser. If you buy something through an online store and submit your credit card number, your Web browser first asks the Web site for its public key, which it uses to negotiate another key, called a *session key*, to encrypt your credit card number on its way through the Internet. The big benefit of this technique is that you don't need to make any prior arrangements with the Web site you're transacting with—all of the negotiation occurs on the spot, yet the information is almost completely secure.

Behind the scenes, the Web site provided its public key in the form of a *digital certificate*. This is a special message that contains not only the Web site's public key, but also the name of the Web site (and the company that owns it), plus a digital signature. Your Web browser uses the digital signature to ensure that the public key truly belongs to the Web site it is trying to access.

But how? Once again, public-key cryptography saves the day. Each certificate is issued by a trusted company called a *certification authority* (CA), which verifies all of the Web site's information ahead of time, converts it all into a large, nearly-unique number called a *digest*, encrypts the digest with its own private key, then throws everything into a certificate which it gives to the Web site operator. (The encrypted digest is the digital signature). When your Web browser receives the certificate, it computes the digest, then decrypts the certificate's signature (using the certification authority's public key) and compares the two digests. If they're the same, the Web browser—and you—is assured that the public key matches the Web site's name. Your browser also checks to see that the Web site's name, as claimed in the certificate, is correct.

So, we return to PGP. Although a full-blown PGP implementation has all of these features available, the most important for an Amateur Radio appli-

Figure 8.1—The *IRLP* authentication process, using PGP digital signatures. Each node has a copy of the master key ring, which is a list of the public keys for each node on the network. The key ring is updated when new nodes join the system. Each node also stores its own private key, which it keeps secret.

cation is authentication. This is the feature of PGP that is used by *IRLP* (**Figure 8.1**). When two *IRLP* nodes establish a connection, they exchange digitally signed messages. To authenticate itself, each node generates a random message, creates a "digest" of it, encrypts the digest with its private key (a process known as *signing*) and sends it to its partner. The partner verifies the signature by decrypting the digest with the sender's public key, and making sure it matches the message. If everything checks out, the partner can be reasonably certain of the sender's identity.

Although PGP can use digital certificates to exchange public keys, a simpler approach is to have each node keep a *keyring*, a list of every other node's number and public key. When your node is added to the *IRLP* network, your node number and public key is added to every other node's keyring by the *IRLP* system. In effect, the *IRLP* system, by distributing your new public key, is assuring other *IRLP* nodes that you are who you say you are, whenever your *IRLP* node connects to another over the Internet. This is similar to the role of the CA in the secure Web conversation described earlier.

SOFTWARE UPDATES

If you're running an *IRLP* node, one thing you can be sure of is that the *IRLP* software is always up to date. That's because *IRLP* is designed to "phone home" each night, check to see if any new software is available, and if so, to download it and install it.

To keep the updates efficient (and reliable), they're distributed across a set of synchronized "slave" servers, rather than just one. Each node's IRLP software selects an appropriate server from the list of the ones on-line, and then logs into that server to receive the updates. Distributing the load in this fashion helps ensure that the system will "scale" well as the number of nodes continues to grow.

Most of the time, the only thing that needs updating are the database files—the master list of nodes and addresses on the system, and the corresponding master keyring with each node's public key. Each node also keeps an updated copy of the "connect" and "disconnect" audio messages for every other node, since the node originating the connection plays them over the local link. For the most part, these updates execute swiftly and silently, without the need for periodic maintenance.

One useful feature of these nightly updates is that every IRLP node carries with it all of the necessary information to establish a connection with every other node, without the continuous need for a central server. Although the odds are slim that every slave server would be unavailable, the IRLP software is designed to fall back to local files if none of the main servers is reachable. The only nodes not contactable in that scenario would be those whose IP address had changed recently, or those that had just been added to the system since the last nightly update.

The nightly updates are scheduled and kicked off by a *Linux* daemon called **cron**. **cron** can also be used to run custom scripts on custom schedules. For example, you could set up your own **crontab** entries to enable and disable your node at certain times of day, or to automatically connect and disconnect to other nodes or reflectors. **cron** is simple but very flexible.

CUSTOM SCRIPTS

After installing *IRLP*, you'll find that the installer has created a directory called **/home/irlp/custom**. This is the place to put any custom scripts you create, to keep them separate from the "stock" scripts and binaries supplied with the *IRLP* package. This keeps everything organized, and helps ensure that the periodic automatic software updates don't affect your customizations.

Although scripts for *IRLP* can be written in a variety of different languages, such as *Perl*, it's most commonly done as a *shell script*. A shell script is a script that's executed by the *command shell*, the same program that accepts your commands from the keyboard. *Unix*-like systems such as *Linux* can use any of several different shells, but the default for *Linux* is **bash** (which stands for "Bourne-again shell", since its language is compatible with the Bourne shell). The first line of each script is a special comment that indicates which program should interpret the script.

An example of a simple *IRLP* shell script is shown in **Figure 8.2**. This script keys the link transmitter, plays a WAV file through the sound card (and over the link), and then un-keys. The script takes one argument, namely, the name of the WAV file (without the extension).

Of course, to really be useful, the script could be enhanced to check to be sure the link is neither transmitting nor receiving before playing the sound, and either to exit or to wait until the transmission is complete.

To create a new script, use a text editor (such as **vi** or **pico**) to build a text file containing the script commands, and then mark the file as executable using the **chmod** command. Ideally, you should mark the file as owner-executable, and change the owner of the file to **repeater**, the username under which *IRLP* utilities run, using **chown**.

For example:
cd /home/irlp/custom

pico myscript   [edit the file, save it, and exit]

chmod 750 myscript

chown repeater myscript

```
#!/bin/bash

. /home/irlp/custom/environment          # Set up the shell environment.

$BIN/key                                 # Begin transmitting.

usleep 2000                              # Wait 2 seconds.

$BIN/play $AUDIO/$1.wav >&/dev/null 2>&1  # Play the WAV file, and wait till
finished.

$BIN/unkey                               # Release the PTT.
```

Figure 8.2—A simple *IRLP* shell script.

```
#!/bin/bash

# This is the custom decode file. Make sure all valid codes exit with "exit
1".

# Standard enable/disable codes.
if [ "$1" = "12001" ] ; then "$SCRIPT"/disable ; exit 1 ; fi
if [ "$1" = "12002" ] ; then "$SCRIPT"/enable ; exit 1 ; fi

# Key and un-key the AUX1 output of the interface board.
if [ "$1" = "*711" ] ; then "$BIN"/aux1on ; exit 1 ; fi
if [ "$1" = "*710" ] ; then "$BIN"/aux1off ; exit 1 ; fi

exit 0
```

Figure 8.3—Example of a custom_decode script.

One special script in the custom directory is **custom_decode**. This is the place to put the codes for any custom DTMF functions you'd like to implement. Each time a sequence of DTMF digits is received, the *IRLP* software calls this script. The script can compare the incoming DTMF string against any number of special combinations, and if found, take some sort of action in response. The software checks the script's exit code to determine whether to run default processing on the DTMF sequence. If the exit code is 0, it means (presumably) that the digits didn't match any of the custom functions, and should be acted on by the main *IRLP* decode script. If the exit code is 1, processing of the digits terminates without further action. **Figure 8.3** shows an example of **custom_decode**. If you're planning to create your own version of **custom_decode**, note that the star is encoded as the letter S, the pound sign comes over as P and the D digit cannot be used.

With the right combination of scripts and binaries, you can do just about

```
Oct 04 2003 16:17:19 -0400 Node Enabled
Oct 04 2003 22:58:18 -0400 IRLP call initiated to stn4200
Oct 04 2003 22:58:23 -0400 stn420 reply connectok ADPCM
Oct 04 2003 22:59:06 -0400 Node Disconnect from stn4200
Oct 04 2003 22:59:49 -0400 busy stn4579
Oct 05 2003 17:07:59 -0400 stn5562 connect ADPCM
Oct 05 2003 17:08:42 -0400 stn5562 disconnect
Oct 05 2003 22:52:53 -0400 IRLP call initiated to stn4130
Oct 05 2003 22:52:59 -0400 stn413 reply connectok ADPCM
Oct 05 2003 22:53:11 -0400 Node Disconnect from stn4130
Oct 06 2003 21:13:02 -0400 decode: DTMF = 9990
Oct 06 2003 21:13:04 -0400 Node Connected to reflector echo on channel 0
Oct 06 2003 21:13:45 -0400 decode: DTMF = 73
Oct 06 2003 21:13:46 -0400 Node Disconnect from ref9990
Oct 06 2003 22:40:44 -0400 decode: DTMF = 5406
Oct 06 2003 22:40:45 -0400 IRLP call initiated to stn5406
Oct 06 2003 22:40:50 -0400 stn5406 reply connectok ADPCM
Oct 06 2003 22:41:51 -0400 decode: DTMF = 73
Oct 06 2003 22:41:52 -0400 Node Disconnect from stn5406
```

Figure 8.4—A portion of a typical *IRLP* log file.

anything. The binaries provided with *IRLP* (in the **/home/irlp/bin** directory) take care of interacting with the interface board and the VoIP system, but if you're familiar with programming, you can certainly create your own binaries to drive other peripherals that might be connected.

Taken to an extreme, one interesting (and useful) project would be a full-blown repeater controller that runs on *Linux* and interfaces with receivers, transmitters, and other equipment through the computer's serial, parallel, or USB ports. The program could even handle remote control and autopatch through voice-modem devices, and the whole thing could be built with *IRLP* baked right in from the beginning! As you can see, the possibilities—just like our Amateur Radio project lists—are virtually endless.

For more examples of custom *IRLP* scripts, check the *IRLP* node owner's group on *Yahoo!* Many of these scripts are fully refined and might be ready to run on your own system without modification.

LOGGING

As it runs, *IRLP* generates a detailed log file of all significant activity. Logs are maintained as ordinary text files in the **/home/irlp/log** directory.

The current log file is called **messages**, and previous log files are renamed to **messages.1**, **messages.2** and so on. A portion of a typical *IRLP* log file is shown in **Figure 8.4**.

An easy way to keep running tabs on your node's activity is to open up a virtual terminal session and enter this command:

tail −f /home/irlp/log/messages

This will display the last 10 lines of the current log file, and continuously update the display as new log entries are added.

Chapter 9

Legal Issues in Linking

There's been a great deal of confusion about the legal aspects of Internet linking. Part of the problem is that very few countries have recognized the concept of Internet linking in their Amateur Radio regulations. In the United States, for example, the Federal Communications Commission's rules governing the Amateur Radio Service make no mention of interconnecting radio transmitters to the Internet. This leaves hams in the position of having to interpret the more general rules relating to station control and third-party traffic.

In certain countries, however, the rules are a bit clearer. In the United Kingdom, for example, the Office of Communications (Ofcom) specifically allows amateurs to operate so-called "voice gateways" if they have obtained a special permit called a Notice of Variation (NoV). This NoV is an endorsement to an Amateur license that gives the licensee permission to operate a VoIP link on a specific frequency in the VHF or UHF bands.

A DISCLAIMER

Before diving into this topic, let me first say that I am not an authority on Amateur Radio regulations around the world, nor am I an attorney. As a licensed Amateur Radio operator, it's your responsibility to read, understand, interpret and comply with the rules that apply to your station, just as I have done. As a starting point, you might be interested in one ham's journey through his country's regulations. So, what follows is *my own view* of how the regulations governing my station should be applied.

STATIONS AND SYSTEMS

One important point should be made right off the bat. Government agencies such as the FCC regulate Amateur *stations*, not *systems*. For example, it would not be accurate to use a phrase such as "the FCC rules about *EchoLink*." The FCC does not regulate *EchoLink*, *IRLP*, *eQSO*, nor any other computer system or software used with Amateur Radio. It does, however, regulate US Amateur Radio stations. So, what we're discussing here is how to legally operate a *station* that happens to have this type of system connected to it.

FCC RULES, PART 97

In the United States, Federal Communications Commission (FCC) rules do not prohibit interconnection of Amateur stations with the Internet. However, the lack of any special regulations for this type of connection would seem to imply that all ordinary operating rules apply to the link station. For example, the link station would need to identify itself every ten minutes, stay within the limits on emission type, power and frequency, and have a designated control operator, just as if the station was not connected to the Internet. In other words, the act of connecting the station by voice to the Internet conveys no special operating rules or privileges.

The first stop is Section 97.3, Definitions. Here are some definitions of particular interest:

6) Automatic control. The use of devices and procedures for control of a station when it is transmitting so that compliance with the FCC Rules is achieved without the control operator being present at a control point.

(7) Auxiliary station. An Amateur station, other than in a message forwarding system, that is transmitting communications point-to-point within a system of cooperating Amateur stations.

(12) Control operator. An Amateur operator designated by the licensee of a station to be responsible for the transmissions from that station to assure compliance with the FCC Rules.

(13) Control point. The location at which the control operator function is performed.

(30) Local control. The use of a control operator who directly manipulates the operating adjustments in the station to achieve compliance with the FCC Rules.

(31) Message forwarding system. A group of Amateur stations participating in a voluntary, cooperative, interactive arrangement where communications are sent from the control operator of an originating station to the control operator of one or more destination stations by one or more forwarding stations.

(38) Remote control. The use of a control operator who indirectly manipulates the operating adjustments in the station through a control link to achieve compliance with the FCC Rules.

(39) Repeater. An Amateur station that simultaneously retransmits the transmission of another Amateur station on a different channel or channels.

(46) Third-party communications. A message from the control operator (first party) of an Amateur station to another Amateur station control operator (second party) on behalf of another person (third party).

INTERNET LINKS: A SPECIAL ANIMAL?

First, what type of station, in the eyes of the FCC, is a VoIP link? Is it a repeater, a message forwarding system, an auxiliary station or none of the above?

Some have argued that a VoIP link counts as a repeater (as long as it's connected to an RF node at the other end), since its sole purpose in life is to retransmit the signals of another Amateur station. (One "benefit," incidentally, of defining it as a repeater is that it would qualify for automatic control.)

However, I see some problems with this. Certainly, when viewing the whole picture end-to-end, it is indeed true that the voice of mobile station A is being re-transmitted on a different channel to mobile station B, through the cooperation of link X and link Y. However, does that mean that Link Y—just one piece of the whole system—is considered a repeater in its own right? Keep in mind that Link X and Link Y are probably being operated under different call signs by different licensees, and might even be in different countries. Unlike a repeater system with remote receivers joined by telephone lines, in which the entire system is operated by one licensee as a single, cohesive system, Link X and Link Y have no regulatory relationship with each other, and (in my view) are not repeaters in their own right.

Others have claimed that a VoIP link counts as an auxiliary station, since it is "transmitting communications point-to-point within a system of cooperating Amateur stations." Maybe we're getting warmer. Systems like *IRLP* and *EchoLink* might qualify as a system of cooperating Amateur stations, and the VoIP link, if it's tuned to the input frequency of a repeater, is certainly participating in point-to-point RF communications. And, most likely, the link licensee has set up his link in cooperation with the repeater licensee, further supporting the "cooperating stations" idea.

But what if the VoIP link is tuned to a simplex frequency rather than a repeater input—can this still be considered point-to-point communication? And would *every* station that fits this broad definition be considered an auxiliary station? If you sit down at your HF rig every night at 8 PM for a sked with a ham in Australia, you are certainly working point-to-point, and the two of you could be regarded as working in cooperation with each other. Does that make your station an auxiliary station, under the FCC's definition? If so, this practice would be illegal, since it occurs below 222.15 MHz!

This is an extreme example, to be sure, but the point is that the FCC's definition of "auxiliary station" is not very precise. It is often understood to apply to special, permanently installed stations that are used to link repeaters (or components of repeaters, such as remote receivers) together, or for RF control links.

However, some amateurs believe the auxiliary-station definition also applies to any station transmitting on the input frequency of a repeater, even if not part of the repeater system *per se*, and even if operated by a different licensee. Others believe that any Internet voice gateway, whether tuned to a repeater input or not, must be considered an auxiliary station, simply because it doesn't fit neatly into other categories. From the licensee's perspective, the "advantage" of such a view is that it would allow links to be automatically controlled, and the "disadvantage" is that it would prohibit them from operating below 222.15 MHz entirely.

But the purpose and spirit of the auxiliary-station definition, in my view, is to allow components of a repeater system (such as remote inputs) to communicate with each other under automatic control, and to ensure that they do not take up valuable spectrum below 222.15 MHz. The automatic-control provision for these auxiliary stations is what makes them practical.

In contrast, an Internet link tuned to the frequency pair of a local repeater uses no additional spectrum at all, regardless of the frequency band. When properly designed, its effect on the spectrum is the same as if it was being operated as a base station by an active ham—possibly even less. As such, it is the licensee's responsibility to ensure that it uses minimal power and doesn't cause harmful interference. Also, I see nothing in §97.3(a)(7) that suggests that the definition would apply to nodes operating on a simplex frequency, communicating with portable and mobile stations in the area.

Fortunately, Part 97 has a general provision for remotely controlled stations. Stated broadly, any U.S. Amateur station may be operated under *remote control* with the same privileges as it may be operated under local control, and under the same set of rules—namely, that a control operator must be monitoring and in control of the station. Remote control can be done either using an auxiliary station, which must be above 222.15 MHz, or over a wireline link. Part 97 says a control link "using a fiber optic cable or another telecommunication service is considered wireline," so sending commands over a telephone line or over an Internet connection certainly seems to suffice. Under this provision, it seems that a VoIP link could be operated on any frequency available to both the control operator and the station licensee, as long as the control operator was always on duty, and had one of these methods of controlling the station remotely.

A question is often asked about the practice of sending DTMF commands over the input frequency of a 2-meter node. Wouldn't this be considered a control function, and therefore illegal below 222.15 MHz?

For one thing, I think there is a distinction here between a control *function* and a control *requirement*. For remotely controlled stations, the FCC requires that a control link exist between the control point and the station, "sufficient for the control operator to perform his/her duties." The definition of remote control in §97.3 refers to making station adjustments over this link to achieve compliance with the Rules. And §97.109(c) says simply "when a station is being remotely controlled, the control operator must be at the control point."

I interpret this to mean that the purpose of the control link is to help prevent the station from operating illegally—for example, to shut it down if it begins drifting off frequency, or if a conversation of a commercial nature takes place—and to have a sure-fire mechanism in place to do so. This doesn't necessarily mean that *all* control functions must be executed over this link, or that every station that sends control signals is performing the duty of the control operator. In summary, the Rules are clear about what constitutes a legal control link, and in which situations it is required, but do not appear to restrict the methods of station control beyond the basic requirement.

Secondly, the control functions commonly available to mobile and portable users through their DTMF keypad are usually not station control functions, strictly speaking. For the most part, these are signals for establishing and dropping Internet connections, rather than signals for switching a transmitter on and off or changing its frequency and power. What is being controlled is not the station (i.e., the transmitter), but the Internet connection behind it.

CONTROL OPERATORS AND THIRD PARTIES

So far so good—the VoIP link is under remote control. What then, is the role of the person that's communicating through it over the Internet? Is that person a control operator, a third party or neither?

Some VoIP enthusiasts argue that the remote person is indeed a control operator, performing his or her duties remotely over the Internet. The trouble with this viewpoint is that the remote person doesn't have much control over the link, beyond disconnecting himself from it, or making it transmit. He might not even know what frequency it is operating on, nor at what power level, nor have any way of monitoring it to verify that it's working right. What's more, he might not even be qualified to be a control operator. Keep in mind that the remote station might be in a different country. FCC Rules *do* specifically allow hams in other countries to be control operators of US stations, but only if a reciprocal operating agreement is in place.

Another possibility is that the remote person is considered a third party, similar to a non-ham speaking over a repeater through a phone patch. Since a control operator is present, it certainly seems legal under Part 97. Can a licensed ham be considered a third party? Nothing in the Rules seems to disallow it. Do international third-party prohibitions apply? Not in my view. Section 97.115, which describes the third-party traffic restrictions, says "An Amateur station may transmit messages for a third party to…any station within the jurisdiction of the United States." If you are operating a VoIP link on a VHF or UHF frequency well within the borders of the US, this is almost certain to be the case! The Rules do not place any restrictions on where the third party is located, only to where the RF transmissions are going. In this case, the long-haul, international path is indeed the public telecommunications system, rather than Amateur Radio.

Could the remote person be *neither* a control operator, *nor* a third party? I think in order for this to work, the remote person would have to be considered a *station*. This raises a couple of issues. It wouldn't apply if the remote person were sitting at a computer rather than a transmitter, since he wouldn't be emitting any RF of his own. And if the remote person is indeed operating a transmitter, as would be the case if he were working through a VoIP link at the other end, it's still complicated by the fact that his audio is being relayed over the Internet rather than being picked up by a receiver directly connected to the local VoIP link.

The upshot of all of this is that I would regard most VoIP links in the United States as ordinary Amateur stations, not repeater stations or auxiliary stations. This means that the link must be either locally or remotely controlled whenever it's on the air. And that means there *must* be a control operator on duty when the link is transmitting, albeit someone listening at a distant control point.

If it's remotely controlled, the licensee (in the US) has the option of using either an RF control link or a wireline link for remote control. An RF control link must be an auxiliary station, and therefore in the 222-MHz band or above, and a wireline link can be either a conventional phone line or an Internet connection. Regardless of the type, there needs to be a 3-minute timer that shuts down the system automatically in case the control link goes dead. (A common implementation of this rule is to have a timer that limits any single transmission to 3 minutes.)

I also acknowledge that *some* VoIP links might qualify as auxiliary stations in their own right. But I think that in order to qualify, they would need to part of a connection involving two or more repeaters within a "system of cooperating Amateur stations"; in order to be legal, they would have to be operating above 222.15 MHz; and in order to be automatically controlled, they could not carry third-party traffic.

STATION IDENTIFICATION

A frequently asked question about VoIP nodes concerns station identification. How, and when, should a node identify itself?

First, let's look at the link station itself. Again, I'll focus on the FCC rules as an example. The answer certainly seems to be that a VoIP node should identify itself just like any other Amateur station—with its own station call sign, "at the end of each communication, and at least every ten minutes during a communication." It makes no difference whether the link is tuned to a simplex frequency or the input frequency of a repeater. Assuming you take the position that the link is neither an auxiliary station nor a repeater, the ID should simply be the station's call sign, with no special suffix. And note that there is no requirement that the station's call sign be the same as that of the repeater to which it is tuned—these are two separate stations in the eyes of the FCC. Finally, note that the call sign of the control operator makes no difference; the ID should be the call sign of the link station itself.

Now, let's consider the VoIP user at the other end, who is working through the link over the Internet. Nothing about the nature of the VoIP connection affects the ID rules. If the remote user were working through a local repeater or simplex frequency, he would identify his station in the usual fashion, by announcing his call sign. If he's sitting in front of a computer microphone, no station ID rules apply, since he's not operating an Amateur Radio station. (However, it's become common practice to use one's own call sign periodically in that situation, just as when operating on the air, to help keep track of who is speaking to whom.)

FCC rules allow a radiotelephone station to identify itself either by phone (which includes modulated Morse) or CW. Although a voice ID is usually faster than Morse, the advantage of a Morse ID is that it can be sent simultaneously with speech, so that it takes no additional transmission time.

THE FUTURE

Regulations do change as technology evolves. Witness the FCC rule changes to accommodate ASCII in the early 1980s, and digital message forwarding systems soon thereafter. Internet linking has already earned its stripes as an innovation that benefits the Amateur Radio Service, so perhaps it now deserves special consideration in Part 97.

Chapter 10

Is This Really Ham Radio?

Next to the code/no-code debate, the legitimacy of Internet linking has been one of the most hotly debated topics in Amateur Radio recently. And perhaps with good reason. Interconnecting Amateur Radio with the Internet isn't something that should be taken lightly, nor is it just a minor ripple in the pond of ham radio developments. In some ways, it's a fundamental shift in the way Amateur Radio is perceived.

The obvious problem is that the Internet is not radio. With a few exceptions, the web of the Internet is mostly strung of fiber and copper, with bridges, routers, switches and modems in place of mixers, RF amplifiers, filters and antennas. RF experimenters such as we are apt to view the Internet as a competitor to radio. Certainly, it competes for our time. We feel this all too well as we sit in front of our e-mail programs and Web browsers when we could be spinning the dial in the ham shack instead. We also feel it when we hear our friends and neighbors talking about the wonders of Internet communication, yet returning a blank stare when we ask them if they know about what Amateur Radio can do. Only a few years ago, the response was likely to be, "Is that like CB?" Nowadays, even CB radio is unfamiliar to the public.

Of course, we know better. Having experienced it first-hand, we know that radio is the best way—sometimes, the *only* way—to get the message through in times of disaster. We know that traffic nets trump phone calls (and chat rooms) for efficiency every time. When the power goes out, most of our computers go down, but many of our radios stay up. Our radios aren't susceptible to viruses, worms, denial-of-service attacks or becoming disconnected in the middle of a long, important message. And they work a lot better in the car, and in our hands, than most wireless Internet devices do.

But still, there are some marvelous things the Internet can do. The path from New York to Sydney isn't always good on 20-meter phone, but it's almost always perfect over e-mail. Compared to HF radio, the information rate is enormous—hundreds of megabits per second, potentially, rather than one kilobit. Noise isn't a problem, and the only interference is the steady stream of junk e-mail. In today's world, at least, nothing is more efficient than the Internet, in terms of cost and speed, for moving a message from Point A to Point B, a great distance apart, with no loss of information.

I have pointed out to a few fellow hams that a time-traveling ham, who went to sleep in 1964 and woke up in 2004, might flip on the switch of an HF rig and declare that nothing had changed. Of course, this is an exaggeration— the proportion of AM, SSB, and CW signals have changed, and certainly, the digital mode frequencies have a different flavor than the RTTY signals back then. But essentially, the activities of ragchewing, nets and DXing are about the same as they were 40 years ago, and the modes most widely used on HF are still about the same. The equipment is a lot different (smaller, lighter, cooler, and probably better), but except for digital modes, the basic technology of communicating from one place to another is no more effective or efficient than it was in 1964.

Yet, during this time, communications technology has grown by leaps and bounds. The problem is that (arguably), the most dramatic innovations in recent years haven't been strictly about radio. Two interesting examples are wireless networking and cellular telephones. Both have been exploding in popularity in recent years in consumer markets. And guess what—both involve interconnecting RF devices with landlines, to achieve improved communications.

Why shouldn't Amateur Radio be part of this revolution? Hams, as always, have a great deal to contribute, and are absolute wizards at putting together pieces of a system to create something that's better than the sum of its parts.

In the first chapter of this book, I cited some recent examples of how the role of Amateur Radio in public service and emergency communications was greatly enhanced by its ability to harness the Internet. Even in the short history of Amateur Internet linking, there have been plenty of examples:

• The disaster relief team working in North Carolina in the aftermath of Hurricane Isabel in the fall of 2003 made "extensive use" of *EchoLink* via a portable repeater. The 20-meter Salvation Army Team Emergency Network (SATERN) net then provided HF liaison for travel into the primary disaster area.

• In July of 2003, WX4NHC, at the National Hurricane Center in Miami, received Claudette weather and damage reports from affected areas via both the HF Hurricane Watch Net and portable stations linked through the *IRLP* SKWARN reflector.

• Using a repeater in Louisiana linked to others across the state via *IRLP*, W4EHW was able to collect weather reports during 2003's Hurricane Lili from stations in the affected area that did not have HF radios.

• A supertyphoon struck Guam in December of 2002. After several unsuccessful attempts to reach the island on HF, SATERN finally made contact via an *EchoLink* connection, and used it as a communications link between Guam and the SATERN national office in Chicago.

The first section of Part 97 of the FCC rules is called "Basis and purpose." Even if you live outside of the FCC's jurisdiction, this section is an excellent outline of Amateur Radio's reason-for-being. It is quoted below. As you read through the items in §97.1, think about how Internet linking systems—the interconnection of Amateur Radio and the Internet—help to support these principles:

(a) Recognition and enhancement of the value of the Amateur service to the public as a voluntary noncommercial communication service, particularly with respect to providing emergency communications.

(b) Continuation and extension of the Amateur's proven ability to contribute to the advancement of the radio art.

(c) Encouragement and improvement of the Amateur service through rules which provide for advancing skills in both the communications and technical phases of the art.

(d) Expansion of the existing reservoir within the Amateur radio service of trained operators, technicians and electronics experts.

(e) Continuation and extension of the Amateur's unique ability to enhance international goodwill.

Over the years, hams have gone from connecting telegraph keys to their radios, to connecting telephone receivers, television cameras, Teletype machines, personal computers and GPS receivers. This has brought us radiotelegraphy, radiotelephony, ATV, RTTY, digital communications, and APRS, respectively, all of which have advanced the state of the art and enhanced both the value of Amateur Radio to the public and its enjoyment by hams.

Let's add the Internet to that list and raise the bar even further. Should it be called "radiodigitalintertelephony"? That's kind of a mouthful. VoIP or Internet Linking seems to be the preferred term.

Whatever you want to call it, please take the ball and run with it. Set up an *IRLP*, *EchoLink*, *eQSO* or *WIRES-II* gateway, and help Amateur Radio remain vibrant in the twenty-first century.

Appendix

WEB RESOURCES

Here are some useful URLs for more information about amateur Internet Linking.

IRLP

Internet Radio Linking Project **www.irlp.net**
IRLP General Information Mailing List **www.irlp.net/mailman/listinfo/irlp**
IRLP Owners' Discussion Group on Yahoo! (English) **groups.yahoo.com/group/irlp/**
Speak Freely (Unix) **sourceforge.net/projects/speak-freely-u/**
Speak Freely on *Linux* (implementation advice) **www.germane-software.com/SpeakFreely/**

EchoLink

EchoLink **www.echolink.org**
EchoLink Software Documentation **www.echolink.org/help**
EchoLink Discussion Group on Yahoo! (English) **groups.yahoo.com/group/echolink/**
EchoLink Community Message Board (English) **www.echolinker.com**
EchoLink Map Project **www.echolinkmap.org**

WIRES-II

WIRES-II (English) **www.vxstd.com/en/wiresinfo-en/**

eQSO

eQSO **www.eqso.com**

Other Software

theBridge (conference server) **cqinet.sourceforge.net**
EchoMac (*EchoLink*-compatible program for Mac OS X) **www.dogparksoftware.com/EchoMac.html**

FURTHER READING

Standards and Requests for Comments (RFCs)

RFC 3550 - RTP: A Transport Protocol for Real-Time Applications

Describes RTP, the real-time transport protocol. RTP "provides end-to-end network transport functions suitable for applications transmitting real-time data, such as audio, video or simulation data, over multicast or unicast network services." RTP is the low-level protocol commonly used for sending audio and video streams over digital networks such as the Internet. Downloadable from **www.faqs.org/rfcs**.

RFC 3551 - RTP Profile for Audio and Video Conferences with Minimal Control

A companion to RFC 3550; describes how audio and video data may be carried within RTP. It defines a set of standard encodings and their names when used within RTP. Downloadable from **www.faqs.org/rfcs**.

RFC 2326 - Real Time Streaming Protocol (RTSP)

The Real Time Streaming Protocol, or RTSP, is "an application-level protocol for control over the delivery of data with real-time properties. RTSP provides an extensible framework to enable controlled, on-demand delivery of real-time data, such as audio and video." Downloadable from **www.faqs.org/rfcs**.

Interim European Telecommunication Standard prI-ETS 300 036
Global System for Mobile Telecommunication (GSM)

The official specification of the GSM 06.10 RPE-LTP compression algorithm used by many VoIP systems. Can be ordered from ETSI (European Telecommunications Standards Institute); **www.etsi.org**

ITU-T Recommendation G.726

The standard for Adaptive Differential Pulse Code Modulation (ADPCM), a compression technique for digital voice signals used in many VoIP systems. Can be purchased from the International Telecommunications Union (ITU); **www.itu.int**

ITU-T Recommendations Q.23 and Q.24

Defines "Multifrequency push-button signal" transmission and reception, also known as DTMF. Outlines the technical requirements for generation (Q.23) and detection (Q.24) of DTMF signals. Can be purchased from the International Telecommunications Union (ITU); **www.itu.int**

Digital Signal Processing (DSP)

Digital Signal Processing: Principles, Algorithms and Applications (3rd Edition)
John G. Proakis and Dimitris Manolakis. Prentice Hall
An undergraduate-level or graduate-level textbook providing a general introduction to DSP theory and algorithms.

Digital Signal Processing Technology—Essentials of the Communications Revolution
Doug Smith, KF6DX
American Radio Relay League
A presentation of DSP as it applies to communications technology. Discusses sampling, filters and digital coding systems, as well as DSP hardware and software.

C++ Algorithms for Digital Signal Processing (2nd Edition)
Paul M. Embree and Damon Danieli. Prentice Hall PTR
A practical introduction to DSP techniques, with particular emphasis on digital filtering. Includes a CD-ROM with many code samples written in the *C++* programming language.

DSP Primer
C. Britton Rorabaugh. McGraw-Hill Professional
Basic concepts and principles of digital signal processing, with some treatment of linear prediction, adaptive filters and speech processing (such as companding). Includes a CD-ROM with *C++* source and executable *Windows* code.

ECHOLINK KEYBOARD COMMANDS

As an alternative to using *EchoLink* with a mouse, the following commands can be entered from the keyboard:

Key	*Function*
Alt+1	Activates the Station List area
Alt+2	Activates the Text Message area
Alt+3	Activates the QSO Status area
Alt+4	Activates the Text Chat area
F6	Activates the next area (in the sequence above)
Shift-F6	Activates the previous area (in the sequence above)
Alt+PgDn	Switches between Index View and Explorer View in the Station List
Tab	Switches between the left and right sides of Explorer View, or between sections of the Text Chat area
Space	Begins (or ends) transmitting
Ctrl+F10	Keys (or un-keys) the local transmitter (Sysop mode)
Ctrl+F9	Simulates COS function of local receiver (Sysop mode)

Alt+A	Alarms
Alt+B	List Me As Busy
Ctrl+C	Copy
Alt+C	Connect (the selected station)
Alt+D	Disconnect
Alt+E	Setup
Ctrl+F	Find
Alt+M	Server Message
Ctrl+O	Connect To...
Ctrl+P	Print
Alt+P	Preferences
Alt+R	Reconnect
Ctrl+V	Paste
Ctrl+Z	Undo
Del	Delete
Ctrl+X	Cut
F1	Help (Contents)
Alt+F4	Exit
Alt+F10	Alarm Log
Alt+F11	Station Summary
Alt+F12	Statistics
Alt+F2	Recording start/stop
F5	Refresh (station list)
Alt+F9	DTMF Pad
Alt+Y	Sysop Setup

EXPLORER VIEW SHORTCUTS

The following keyboard commands are available when *EchoLink's* Explorer View is active:

Key	*Function*
Enter	Connect to selected station, or expand selected folder
Tab	Switch between left and right sides of Explorer View
UpArrow	Select previous item in list
DownArrow	Select next item in list
RightArrow	Expand selected folder (left side)
LeftArrow	Collapse selected folder (left side)
* (on num pad)	Expand selected folder and all sub-folders (left side)
PgUp	Scroll to the previous page of items
PgDn	Scroll to the next page of items

Is It Legal?

By Brennan Price, N4QX and ARRL General Counsel Chris Imlay, W3KD

What Part 97 regulations govern VoIP-assisted Amateur Radio?

All of them or none of them, depending on whether you're asking about the "VoIP-assisted" or the "Amateur Radio" part of VoIP-assisted Amateur Radio.

Many callers to the ARRL's Regulatory Information Branch over the last few years have focused on the novelty of the Internet when asking questions about the legal uses of certain systems. Such focus is misdirected. Part 97 does not regulate systems; it regulates stations. The Commission doesn't care what a ham has feeding his or her station; it cares that the *station*—not the Internet, but the *station*—is properly operated. And all the rules that apply to any Amateur Radio station apply to one that retransmits audio fed to it by VoIP.

Fine, so the Commission doesn't care about the VoIP part. Are there any particular rules a ham considering such an operation should be aware of?

The obvious answer is *all of them*, but we'll focus on a few that are easy to overlook, particularly for stand-alone, single channel operations. The main points to remember:

- All stations must be controlled.
- Only certain types of stations may be automatically controlled.
- Simplex voice operations do not qualify for automatic control.
- Any station that is remotely controlled via radio must utilize an auxiliary station to execute said control, and auxiliary stations are restricted in frequency.

It's not as hard as it sounds. All you have to do is think about the type of station you're operating and how it's controlled. Let's look at a few examples.

Two automatically controlled repeaters are linked via VoIP. Is this legal?

Forget the VoIP linking, because that's the Internet. We're talking about two repeaters. Are repeaters legal? Yes. May repeaters be automatically controlled? Yes. There is no difference between this setup and two repeaters linked by another wired mechanism or by auxiliary stations. Assuming the two linked stations are repeaters, it is difficult to conceive of a situation where a VoIP link would not pass regulatory muster. The only caveat is that the VoIP software must prevent nonhams from accessing the repeaters from the Internet. The key here is to avoid any configuration that would (1) permit a nonham to key an amateur transmitter without the presence of a control operator, and (2) prevent the initiation by a nonham of a message via an Amateur Station without the presence of a control operator.

Is it permitted to enable *automatically controlled* simplex nodes?

No. Only certain types of Amateur Radio stations may be operated unattended, under *automatic control*. This means that there is no human control either at the station location or at a distance. These types of stations are space stations, repeaters, beacons, auxiliary stations and certain types of stations transmitting RTTY or data emissions.

Simplex VoIP nodes are neither repeaters, beacons nor auxiliary stations. Presumably, most are within 50 kilometers of the Earth's surface and are therefore not space stations. The VoIP technology implies a voice transmission, not RTTY or data. Therefore, none of the stations that qualify for automatic control describe a simplex VoIP node, and such a station must be locally or remotely controlled (as *any* Amateur Radio station is allowed to be).

Locally or remotely controlled—what does that mean?

A simplex VoIP node may be locally controlled by an operator who is present at the node. Such a node may also be *remotely controlled* at some other point, with the operator issuing commands via a wireline or radio control link. If a radio control link is used, it must utilize an auxiliary station, and such stations are restricted in frequency to 222.15 MHz and above (with the exception of the CW, SSB and amateur satellite portions of the 70-cm band). It's this *remotely controlled* aspect that allows VoIP simplex nodes to operate legally—as long as they are on the right bands.

Let's consider seven scenarios:

• A control operator is stationed and active at the VoIP node on any frequency. This is a locally controlled station, not at all unlike a typical operation on FM simplex. ***This is legal.***

• A control operator communicates with and controls a simplex VoIP node with a handheld, transmitting and listening to the node on 223.52 MHz. This is wireless remote control. Such control must be executed by an auxiliary station and 223.52 MHz is an allowed frequency for such a station. ***This is legal.***

• A control operator communicates with and controls a simplex VoIP node with a handheld, transmitting and listening to the node on 147.41 MHz. This is wireless remote control. Such control must be executed by an auxiliary station, but 147.41 MHz is *not* an allowed frequency for such a station. ***This operation is not legal.*** It may be made legal by locally controlling the node, choosing a control frequency on which auxiliary station operation is permitted, or controlling the node via a wireline link. The next three examples show each option in action.

• A control operator operates a simplex VoIP node at 147.41 MHz and is stationed at the node's transmitter. User stations access the node on the same frequency. ***This is legal.*** The VoIP node is being locally controlled, and any station may be locally controlled.

• A control operator operates a simplex VoIP node at 147.41 MHz. The control operator continually monitors the node's transmissions and can call a dedicated telephone line or use a dedicated Internet connection to turn the node on and off. User stations access the node on the same frequency. ***This is legal.*** The VoIP node is being remotely controlled via a wireline connection, and any station may be controlled in this manner.

• A control operator communicates with and controls a simplex VoIP node with a multiband handheld, transmitting to and continuously monitoring the node on 147.41 MHz. He or she sends power on/off commands with the same handheld on 223.52 MHz. This is wireless remote control. Such control must be executed by an auxiliary station, and 223.52 MHz is an allowed frequency for such a station. ***This is legal.*** The VoIP node is being remotely controlled via an auxiliary station of appropriate frequency, and any station may be controlled in this manner.

• Same configuration as either of the above two situations, except the control operator does not continuously monitor the VoIP node's transmissions. ***This operation is not legal.*** When a simplex VoIP node is enabled, it must be continually attended, either locally or remotely. A simplex VoIP node is no different than other FM simplex operations, and such operations may not be automatically controlled.

Glossary

ADPCM—Adaptive differential pulse code modulation. A waveform codec that records the difference between samples, rather than their actual values, and adjusts the coding scale dynamically (or uses logarithmic coding).

access control—The process of granting or denying access to resources based on identity.

authentication—The process of identifying a person (or computer) to ensure they are who they claim to be. Successful authentication establishes identity.

buffer—A temporary storage area in a computer's memory. A buffer from which data is read in the same order as it was written is known as a first-in, first-out (FIFO) buffer.

cable modem—An RF modem designed to operate over cable TV lines, or a type of Internet service (provided by cable TV companies) that uses these devices.

codec—Compressor-decompressor. A computer program (or hardware device) that compresses digitized audio or video into a more compact representation, and also decompresses it.

compression—The technique of transforming data into a format that takes up less storage space or less bandwidth. With *lossless* compression, the data retains the same amount of information; with *lossy* compression, the data is approximated.

conference server—A computer program that can interconnect multiple nodes in such a way that transmissions from one node are received by all others. Also called a "reflector" or "conference bridge."

conference—A group of nodes that are currently interconnected by a reflector, a conference server, or a node that supports conferencing. Each such node is said to be "in conference." Transmissions from any participant in the conference are sent to all others.

conferencing—A feature available on some nodes that allows multiple nodes to be joined together in a conference, in the same manner as a conference server. The node's own RF gateway is always a participant in such a conference.

CTCSS—Continuous tone-controlled squelch system. A squelch system that responds to the presence of a low-pitched audio tone, rather than the quieting of the FM receiver, to detect an incoming signal. Motorola's implementation of CTCSS is called PL.

DHCP—Dynamic host configuration protocol. A system for automatically assigning an IP address to a computer when it is first started.

digital certificate—A digitally signed document that contains information about a person or organization, along with the person or organization's public key. It is usually signed by a trusted organization that has verified its authenticity.

digital signature—The digest (digital summary) of a message, encrypted with the sender's private key. With the corresponding public key, the recipient of a message can use the digital signature to verify that the contents of the message have not been altered, and to verify the authenticity of the sender.

DSL—Digital Subscriber Line. A technology that allows digital signals to be carried over twisted-pair telephone lines. Often used to provide Internet access.

DTMF—Dual tone multi-frequency. A signaling system in which digits and special characters are transmitted as pairs of tones over a voice channel. Also called Touch-Tone.

firewall—Computer equipment (or software) that blocks undesired network communication, usually to or from the Internet for security reasons.

forwarding—A feature available in most NAT routers that allows all incoming packets addressed to a specific port to be routed to a specific computer.

GSM—1) A type of digital cellular telephone system. 2) The audio codec developed for this system, which carries voice at 13 kbps.

interface—In the context of Internet linking, a circuit that joins a receiver and transmitter (or transceiver) to a node's computer equipment. The interface usually connects to the computer's serial or parallel port, the computer's sound card, and the microphone, speaker, PTT, and carrier-detect terminals of the transceiver.

IP—Internet protocol. The set of packet-oriented digital communications protocols used by hosts on the Internet and other networks.

jitter—Unpredictable variations in latency over time, usually due to network congestion.

latency—The time it takes for data to move from one point to another through a network, or to be transformed from one form to another.

link—A station that forms a voice gateway between Amateur Radio frequencies and the Internet. Also called an "RF node."

Linux—An open-source, *Unix*-type operating system that runs on many different types of computers, from PCs to mainframes. Some distributions of *Linux* are available free of charge.

NAT—Network address translation. A feature of some routers that allows several computers on a local network to share a single Internet address, by re-addressing incoming and outgoing packets.

net—A conference that is established at a designated time, often to discuss a specific topic.

node—In the context of Internet linking, a computer equipped with VoIP software that can communicate over the Internet with others so equipped. A node can be a station that forms a voice gateway between Amateur Radio frequencies and the Internet, a stand-alone computer that communicates with other nodes over the Internet, or a conference server. An RF node is also called a "link" or "voice gateway."

node number—A number that uniquely identifies a node. VoIP system administrators usually assign node numbers.

NoV—Notice of Variation. A license endorsement granted by the Radiocommunications Agency in the UK. An NoV for Internet Voice Gateway operation is currently required for Amateurs who wish to operate an RF node in the UK.

PCM—Pulse code modulation. A digital representation of an audio signal in which each value is directly proportional to the amplitude of the corresponding sample.

peer—A node that is currently connected to one or more other nodes.

peer-to-peer—Communication that takes place directly from one node to another (over the Internet), rather than through a central server.

PGP—Pretty Good Privacy. A set of cryptographic functions that can be used for encrypting or digitally signing messages that are sent over the Internet.

private key—In public-key cryptography, the key that is kept secret by the sender of a signed message, or by the recipient of an encrypted message. A message signed with the private key can be verified with the matching public key, and a message encrypted with the public key can only be decrypted with the matching private key.

public key—In public-key cryptography, the key that is disclosed by the sender of a signed message, or by the recipient of an encrypted message. A message encrypted with the public key can only be decrypted with the matching private key.

pulseback—A situation in which a node transmits to the Internet due to a false COS signal when the link transmitter goes key-up. The typical cure is to adjust the software's pulseback (or "anti-thump") timer so that it ignores the false COS signal.

reflector—1) An *IRLP* conference server. 2) A computer program that receives e-mail messages and sends a copy of each to every subscriber in a list.

router—A device that connects to two or more networks and relays data from one to another. For example, a router may be installed between the Internet and a local-area network. Most routers can also act as simple firewalls.

script—A computer program, written in a scripting language, to be processed by a script interpreter or shell. Usually, a script is a series of commands that are interpreted and executed line-by-line, rather than being compiled into the native language of the computer.

scripting language—A computer programming language suitable for creating scripts.

trustee—The licensed Amateur responsible for operation of a node. Usually, but not always, the owner of the equipment and/or the licensee of the station.

validation—The process of initial authentication and license verification performed by VoIP system administrators when new users request access to the system.

VoIP—Voice-over-Internet protocol. The technique of using the Internet as a medium to carry voice signals by digitizing the voice, compressing it and sending it as IP packets to a peer.

WAV—A file format, developed by Microsoft and IBM, for storing waveform audio data. A WAV file can contain data encoded in any of several different forms, such as PCM, ADPCM and GSM.

Index

Notes

Notes

Notes

Notes

Notes

FEEDBACK

Please use this form to give us your comments on this book and what you'd like to see in future editions, or e-mail us at **pubsfdbk@arrl.org** (publications feedback). If you use e-mail, please include your name, call, e-mail address and the book title, edition and printing in the body of your message. Also indicate whether or not you are an ARRL member.

Where did you purchase this book?
☐ From ARRL directly ☐ From an ARRL dealer

Is there a dealer who carries ARRL publications within:
☐ 5 miles ☐ 15 miles ☐ 30 miles of your location? ☐ Not sure.

License class:
☐ Novice ☐ Technician ☐ Technician Plus ☐ General ☐ Advanced ☐ Extra

---

Name _____

Daytime Phone (   ) _____

Address _____

City, State/Province, ZIP/Postal Code _____

If licensed, how long? _____

Other hobbies _____

_____

Occupation _____

ARRL member? ☐ Yes ☐ No
Call Sign _____

Age _____

E-mail _____

From _____

_____

_____

EDITOR, INTERNET LINKING FOR RADIO AMATEURS
ARRL—THE NATIONAL ASSOCIATION FOR AMATEUR RADIO
225 MAIN STREET
NEWINGTON CT 06111-1494

— — — — — — — — — — please fold and tape — — — — — — — — — — — — —